Mandala Energy

Manda Greasley

Thinking about my lovely Mum

Thank you, Dean, Eleanor and Sebastian,
for your love

For Yogis who already sit on their mat
and for those thinking about it... yes, you too

Happy 60th Birthday Robin
with love from
Marden +

I love beyond reason
and I understand
that most people can't handle that
I'm too much
too intense
too open
too brave
which more than often
ends in another heartbreak for me
Ouch!
Totally worth it

hellcatsyoga

Mandala
(mand-arh-la)

Noun: a circular shape representing the universe in Hindu and Buddhist symbolism. It attracts energy and represents unity

Sanskrit word for 'circle'.

In Jungian psychology, a mandala is a symbol in a dream, representing the dreamer's search for completeness and self-unity

Energy

'Prana' or 'Chi'
Subtle energy of the body that flows through us and everything around us. The energy that mediates between the physical and emotional aspects of self.

Yoga teaches us to control this energy.

Yoga

Noun: a Hindu spiritual and ascetic discipline, a part of which, includes breath control, simple meditation, and the adoption of specific bodily postures, is widely practised for health and relaxation

Physically:
- If we don't move our bodies as intended - we lose the ability to move our bodies

Mentally:
- We become the person we are meant to be, our true nature

Spiritually:
- The belief that there is something greater than the human self, possibly cosmic or divine

'Yoga' has many translations although the most popular is 'Yoke' or 'Unite'. The Sanskrit word 'Yuj' means to yoke or bind. We're aiming to connect with our true nature through our mind, body and soul. If you don't like the sound of that explanation you can also consider that the word 'yoga' can also mean separation or disentanglement. The thing we're aiming to disentangle from is our own 'prison' or whatever it is that's stopping us from feeling our true nature or feeling liberated

The word in Sanskrit for liberation or freedom is 'Moksha'.

Ahimsa
Non-Violence
- Non harm to ourselves or others
- To value ourselves
- To create self-acceptance and self-love
- To take responsibility for our capacity for violence.
- To practice kindness

How can I be kinder to myself and others?

Satya
Truthfulness
- Truthfulness with self
- Listening to our shadow
- Dialogue with truth
- Living authentically

How can I become more truthful in this moment?

Asteya
Non-Stealing
- Not stealing from others
- Stealing from the earth
- Creating a better future for our children
- Not taking what isn't ours, written, spoken or otherwise
- Less greed, more generosity
- Stepping away from feelings of entitlement

Am I aware of taking what isn't mine?

Aparigraha
Non-Attachment
- Non-greed or possessiveness to people and things
- Non-attachment to people and things
- Letting go
- Being happy with less

Can I enjoy right now instead of overthinking the future?

Brahmacharya
Non-Excess
- Avoiding living in excess
- Healthy, mutually respectful intimate relationships
- Living without obsessions
- Creating a healthy win/win
- Avoiding overindulging
- Stepping away from our ego

What do I use as my own 'self-check?'

Saucha
Cleanliness
- Keeping ourselves and our environment clean
- Removing clutter
- Removing resentment
- Being aware of how we spend our time
- Protecting our land, air, water and the planet's future

How can I keep my thoughts, intentions and environment pure?

Svadhyaya
Self-Study
- Learning from our own experiences
- Practicing curiosity
- Who am I? Who are you?
- Listening to our shadows and acting upon it
- Meditating
- Cultivating self-knowing
- Spending solitary time in nature
- Journaling

Am I continually learning and developing?

Santosa
Contentment

- Bringing ourselves back to the here and now
- Being relaxed
- Knowing we are enough
- Knowing we have enough
- Trusting
- Letting life open before us
- Being in love with our own life
- Not comparing ourselves with others
- Being happy with what is

How can I enjoy this moment, today, knowing I have enough, and that I am enough?

Tapas
Fire or heat

- The fire to ignite change
- To continue our purpose
- To commit to our intention
- To commit to our cause
- Avoiding the escape route
- Transformation instead of distraction
- Taking full responsibility

How can I build my own fire, or paddle my own boat?

Ishvara-Pranidhana
Surrender

- To believe in something bigger than just ourselves
- Living between effort and surrender
- Dedicating our practice to another
- Collective consciousness

Can I surrender and let go?

Chakra
A Sanskrit term, meaning wheel, or vortex.
Spinning energy centres within the body.
Chakra is pronounced 'chuk-kruh' with the 'ch' sound
similar to 'chop', not 'shop'.

Root Chakra - Muladhara
'I am'
Survival, grounding, family, stability, security, support, a
sense of belonging, community.
- When we want to feel safe, secure, passionate,
energetic, balanced, vibrant.
- When we want a sense of community or belonging.
- When we want to feel at home or in our safe retreat.

Sacral Chakra - Svadhisthana
'I feel'
Creativity, relationships, sexuality, empathy, pleasure,
wellbeing, connection, change, emotions.
- When we want to feel confident, connected to
everything around us
- When we want to embrace change or develop
relationships with others.
- When we want to move our bodies and free ourselves.
- When we want to feel pleasure or express our
sexuality.

Solar Plexus Chakra - Manipura
'I do'
Willpower, joy, motivation, self-esteem, transformation,
identity, vitality.
- When we want to feel energised, determined and
powerful.
- When we want to enjoy feeling happy, joyous, hopeful.
- When we desire a sense of empowerment.
- When we want to express our individuality and provide
willpower or drive.

Heart Chakra - Anahata
'I love'

Love, compassion, balanced emotions, open-heartedness, desire for self-acceptance, harmony, forgiveness, gratitude, devotion, nurture, healing.

- When we want to feel loved and nourished.
- When we want to feel rejuvenated or younger.
- When we want to nurture gratitude and all we're thankful for.
- When we want to heal.

Throat Chakra - Vishuddha
'I talk'

Expression, communication, truth, authenticity, integration.

- When we want to speak and hear the truth.
- When we want to be genuine to ourselves
- When we want to feel relaxed, still and steady.
- When we want to feel unified between our internal and external worlds.
- When our hearts and minds are conflicted.

Third Eye Chakra - Ajna
'I see'

Intuition, knowing, perception, wisdom, imagination, meditation, self-reflection.

- When we want to concentrate and focus.
- When we want to cultivate our intuition and wisdom.
- When we want to boost our interpretation, perspective and imagination.

Crown Chakra - Sahasrara
'I understand'

Spiritual connection, consciousness, bliss, unification, purity, divinity, simplicity, clarity.

- When we want to feel calm and cleansed, clear and true.
- When we want to feel connected to all living beings.

Journal entry
Thursday 10th May 2018

'I've always thought of myself as a little weird, different or alternative, when in fact there are others just like me sharing their weirdness much the same. The thing is, we attract each other. As far as my career and making money is concerned, I think it can be a huge trap. We can put all our attention on making it, but we risk compromising our essence and creativity, increasing stress and allowing our life to become something we don't want it to be. I believe that if we do what makes our heart sing, our income will (or won't) materialise but the journey will be more fun. The fact is, if our passion, excitement and purpose is so great, others can't help but be affected by it. Don't go through the sh*t and crap, just flow because flowing is so much easier.
Opportunities will arise. Feel the fear and do it anyway; do what makes your heart sing'.

Prologue

I was seven when my mother told me to go and get changed behind a tree at a local outdoor paddling pool. Thing is, I didn't know where 'behind the tree' was, walking around it I'd be seen by those bathing in front of it, or seen by those walking along the path behind it. It taught me two things; firstly, that I like trees, and secondly, life can be like that – confusing.

I've talked to a lot of people in my professions, and at the age of fifty-five I have come to the conclusion that whatever it looks like from the outside, no one has it all together; not me and not anyone I've spoken to. We're all vulnerable and feel a little lost at times; I think that's the essence of life and being human.

One of my favourite personal development books is titled *The Seven Habits of Highly Effective People* by Stephen Covey. Sadly, Covey passed away a few years ago, however, his son, Sean, has re-released the book with updates and quotes his father saying in jest, that each individual 'habit' was considered the best habit depending on which month of the year it was. Sean points out that our least favourite 'habit' will most likely be the one we're not very good at. Likewise, we tend to avoid jobs and tasks (and yoga poses) we dislike, probably because we're not very good at them. I believe the information within the eight limbs of yoga can identify and create positive habits to help us live a more balanced life.

And so, I tell my story...

As a child, I thought I'd grow up and be adult-like or 'sorted'. As 'sorted' as my parents appeared to be, as 'sorted' as the many non-blood-related 'aunties' I had, or as 'sorted' as my schoolteachers. 'Sorted' to me meant being an adult, having a career, family and running a home, not once did I think of the responsibilities they had or the worries they held. Their children, jobs, homes, relationships and health. But, of course, I was only a child and had no idea what was happening in, and behind the personas of their lives. When we get a little older, we realise that life isn't quite that simple or easy, we start to carry stress, anxiety and emotional baggage, we carry the not so happy experiences from our past along with our frustrations and difficulties; we have challenges mixed with moments of pure happiness and we have days when life feels a struggle. Luckily, or unluckily, our ego works hard to protect us, stopping the outside world from being aware of what's going on and because this is happening, we think everyone else is ok and only we are not. That's when life can get tough and feel a little lonely.

Our ego helps us live our lives by creating beliefs, patterns and ideas, however if we over identify with it, it can take us away from our true nature by inflating what we see in ourselves, what we believe about ourselves and what we perceive to be right. Our ego wants us to look good and show the world we're doing great, but our ego can also stop us from living an authentic life; stop us from being the person we really are.

We often become entangled in our thoughts, ways of living and wants, which confuse our true nature. Our egos push and pull us around creating 'storms' in our minds. If someone is said to have a big ego, we believe them to be a little 'up themselves'. What we're trying to describe, is they identify a little too closely with 'I, Me or My' and get caught up in mental storms more often.

Yoga helps us disentangle ourselves from our ego

Part One

The Tree

My love of trees began when I was very young. My parents worked hard running both a printing business and restaurant; my sister and I amused ourselves during the long summer holidays in the town park. Those were the days when children were safe to play outside; days when children would break their ankles on the see-saw, days when one particular man would sit on the park bench with his penis hanging out of his trouser fly; no-one seemed to do much about it. 'Oh look, there's that strange man again'.

'Manda's stuck up a tree!' shouted my sister after running back to the busy restaurant kitchen. My mother dropped everything, imagining me up one of the park's tall Beech trees, only to find I was stuck up a small coniferous tree that looked more like a bush – yet it felt so high. I'm proud I climbed it that day because the view from the 'top' made life look different. I was very young, but I remember thinking how wonderful it was, seeing a very different angle on life, seeing a 'bigger picture' and a different perspective.

Views broaden our minds and thinking, allowing us to see further, practically, emotionally and spiritually. They help us visualise a future with less boundaries, help us change perspectives and help us create new realities.

A few hundred feet away was the park hall. On Tuesday evenings it was 'Brownie' night. I was eight years old and an Elf, but I wanted to be an Imp, mainly because Imps were yellow, and I like the colour yellow. I remember at that young age not feeling as good as I should have. I wasn't a leader in my 'Six', known as a 'Sixer' or even a 'Seconder' and I embarrassingly only had two badges perched on the shoulder of my uniform, whereas many of the girls' arms were adorned in badges down to their cuffs. Our parents were too busy working into the early hours of the mornings to facilitate our gardening, cooking and pet achievements. It wasn't just the badges; my hair wasn't as long as the other girls either, instead it was 'fashionably' short, mousey and wispy with a shorter than short fringe which my mother assured me, suited me. I looked admiringly at their ponytails and plaits and decided that one day, I'd grow my hair long and brush it at my dressing table similar to Olivia in 'The Waltons' before climbing into bed. So instead, in desperation or frustration, I can't remember, I put a pair of 'American Tan' tights on my head knowing it was as good as it was going to get.

We learn from a very early age to compare ourselves with others. Even during our practice, we find ourselves comparing our ability, but other people are not us, and we are not them.

We lived a happy childhood on a new estate where everyone seemed to know or be familiar with each other, typical of the 1970s. My father was self-employed having left the Royal Air Force and was a talented, intelligent man who was highly creative. He built us our first 'Wendy House' or shed, during our pre-school years and painted nursery rhymes all over it. As we got older, he made us what I would describe as 'a proper shed', which sat at the top of the garden with brick footings, pretty windows, and a front door made from a redundant internal house door. We kept our guinea pigs, mice and hamsters in it and often made beds on the floor sleeping alongside the cages at weekends. It was at this time that my love for sheds and wooden structures started. It's become my #shedfetish

I'm a Hairdresser, accredited Life Coach, Yoga teacher and proud Shed lover. For that reason, I bundled everything together and named my business 'The Head Shed'

There's a specific story that may be truthful or could be just a beautiful story for those of us who dream. Either way, it shares a powerful message that security, belonging and support is an integral part of being human. Its name is the 'African Birth Song'. According to this story, a woman, when aiming to conceive learns a new song. She shares the song with her partner and friends which is learnt over the nine months she is expecting. The song is then sang to her, when she's in labour. That same song is sang at any celebration or when the child becomes ill or hurts itself, likewise if they fall on hard times as an adult, commits a crime or loses their way in life. The song is sang to bring that individual back to their true nature in favour of using punishment. It represents the 'roots' of the person and reminds them of who they are, before finally being sang at their funeral.

Many of us have family and friends living far and wide, some have lost contact with those closest to them. As life unfolds, we often find we have fewer people around us reminding us of our identity and offering support, leaving us to find ways of coping alone.

My father was English and an only child, my mother was German and one of four sisters. Initially, she only spoke German having 'thrown herself in the deep end', she learnt to speak English quickly but maintained her strong German accent to the point where my friends looked at me to ask me what she'd just said, I, of course, didn't hear her accent at all and questioned their confusion. We were part of a lovely local community however, we had no extended family and no connection to a church or any other community. I had a happy childhood but looking back, we had busy entrepreneurial parents, the three of us, my elder sister and younger brother became extremely independent people.

We grow older but remain the children we were inside. I've now lost my parents and, apart from when I am standing next to their graveside, there are few around me to remind me of who I am during shaky times.

'Just like a tree, I am deeply rooted and supported by Mother Earth. I am connected to a deeper purpose.'

– Mala Collective

Conditioning

My sister, just eighteen months older than me, was in an impressive form ten at high school. She was chosen to do the grown-up or more 'responsible' tasks at home, whilst I was asked to do jobs such as ... wait for it ... open the curtains, which later became a bit of a family joke. I constantly got out of jobs like drying the pots after dinner saying I desperately needed to go to the toilet. I got away with too much and that made me think I was smart and savvy. It also had a backlash, secretly making me believe I wasn't capable of doing anything challenging or difficult. My self-esteem as a child must have been low as was my expectation to do well.

When I turned eleven and attended the same high school as my sister, I was put in two forms lower than I'd expected. I stood shocked, whilst it was confirmed; standing there in my 'egg smelling' physics form room, I went into denial, thinking they must have made a mistake.

We were put in a form and that form had a number. The higher the number, the more intelligent you were perceived to be, either that or your father was a doctor. The lower the number, the fewer invitations you had to join anything interesting and the less likely you were to be invited into the school band – possibly not true but that's how it felt. That number identified each of us and stayed with us for years and well into our adult lives. I was in form six; middle of the road. Form six students didn't have fathers who were doctors and weren't invited into the band. I believe it was the start of my conditioning; thinking I wouldn't achieve very much, so at that age I began not to bother.

'We see the world, not as it is, but as we are
- or, as we are conditioned to see it.'

- *Stephen Covey.*
The Seven Habits of Highly Effective People

The thing is, we're all products of our past. Some of the not so positive experiences and memories create and mould the people we are today. We can recognise and accept these memories and change our beliefs around them, or continue to process them and allow them to affect us. In which case we risk sabotaging our lives repeatedly.

I've written this book for those with an interest in yoga and those who have a curious mind. It's also for those who might identify with the highs and lows of life that we want to remember, grow upon, soothe or forget altogether, and for those who have reached a crossroads and want an injection of energy before pursuing a new direction.

In my experience, practicing yoga changes our psyche and how we think about life. The aesthetic outcome of yoga asana is just a by-product – be it a welcome one.

To the outside world, I'm often told 'You're sorted Manda - you're tough, you're confident - you're formidable', even. Really? Someone once said to me 'God chose you to have a poorly child because he knew you could handle it'. Thank you, I suppose that was meant well but those were tough years and I'd rather believe that things happen in life because life isn't perfect and comes with no guarantees, rather than the thought that some of us are chosen to worry themselves sick whilst others are allowed to enjoy a less worrying life - not to mention the effect it has on the child or adult who has to cope with the physical and mental aspects of an ongoing illness. I struggled many times over the years when I needed support. I put on a brave face too many times, I was strong when I wanted to fall apart, and I wouldn't allow myself to cry in fear of what might come after crying. I allowed others to have these beliefs about me because I had to believe them myself.

'Fake it until you make it' is a common quote which I believe works, but it doesn't allow us to be our authentic and honest selves; it doesn't allow us to feel, grounded and safe and it brings limited feelings of security.

Maybe you can relate to some of this? We protect ourselves in the name of appearing strong, appearing perfect, appearing efficient, being liked by others and trying our hardest, whilst at the same time aiming to raise or maintain our self-esteem, as a result, we end up quietly suffering for it.

We can't do anything about what was, but we can do something about how we want to navigate our lives moving forwards. Through the practice of yoga, we can stop the mental struggle, we can learn to let go, and we can create a much easier life.

Our yoga mats are available 24/7. They wait patiently until we choose to use them. Our mat is a safe place, an honest place, a place we can go to any time we like, a place to continually grow both physically and mentally. It's like a home that doesn't need much cleaning, I call it 'a retreat.'

Balance

I was lucky to have my parents well into my forties, but was devastated when they both passed away in a relatively short period of time. Around that time my children grew up and both went to university in Leeds. My attention briefly turned to our dog until we had to have him put to sleep, at the grand age of fifteen. It felt like one loss after the next.

It was as though life had caught up with me. Having and raising my children was and is the best thing that has happened to me. I worked from home fitting in with my family and suddenly there was a big space! It felt frightening because I had no idea what was 'next'. My sister recently found an old schoolbook, which she'd written at the age of nine, about our family. She described me at the age of eight as someone who 'likes playing with her dolls and loves animals'. Sounds a bit boring doesn't it? But it described me perfectly.

All of a sudden, the house had a quietness and stillness about it, even a builder who worked here for some time mentioned how quiet the lane and house was. Quietness forced me to look within.

Want to hear what's going on? Embrace quietness.

I was already an accredited coach with new time to spare, so I focused on myself and began working on getting to know who the new me was. Firstly, I started writing a journal; just a scribble pad and writing down each day how I felt. I banned myself from watching anything less than informative on television, even if it was whilst I was doing other jobs. I also decided to become aware of how I was using my time throughout the day and address what I could do more of, less of, start, or stop.

I'd travelled in a big psychological circle regarding my hairdressing business as I'd been hugely frustrated with the constant act of making others look 'aesthetically pleasing' whilst in contrast, we were desperately trying to save our daughter's eyesight. I started to care less about what I or anyone looked like as someone who is partially sighted, or blind won't judge you on how you look. My opinion changed again the day we sat with a young lady who had, that week, undergone ground-braking surgery to reinstate her sight. She had been blind for over two years. Her mother and I had often chatted in the waiting room. We were fortunate to sit beside them again. I asked Charlotte, 'What was the first thing you did when you got home?'

She was shy at first and after being prompted by her mother 'You can tell Manda and Ellie', she told us she went to her bedroom and styled her hair and put on some of her Mum's makeup. With that, my feelings of anxiety around the subject stopped, and I created a new appreciation for hairdressing realising we all have a desire to look nice whether we can see ourselves or not and if we can, we must cherish and value that ability.

Choices

One of the benefits of coaching is to help 'increase our choices'. Maybe, turning this on its head; by increasing our choices we create more anxiety in deciding which route to take? Our grandparents didn't have the choices we have today, and they possibly accepted 'what is' a little more easily than we do. Our westernised and often middle-class choices have brought much unhappiness when 'Tosha', the Sanskrit word for contentment, could be the right approach instead. The question here is, do we need more choices, or, do we benefit more by putting our attention on what we already have?

Most people are drawn to yoga initially because of the physicality. Not realising that it can change the way we think about life.

I want to share with you some of what I've learnt through my own experiences, through my interpretation of the Eight Limbs of Yoga, the Seven Chakras and some interesting, informative and helpful personal development theories which in my opinion sit nicely alongside the ancient philosophies of yoga. I wish to build, enjoy and benefit from a community where we can appreciate like-minded people, share our energy and feel relaxed enough to sing our unique and personal songs.

Yoga is about creating balance. If you're naturally introverted, it'll help you express yourself. If you're naturally extroverted, it'll help you find peace. If you're a physical person, it'll help you find stillness. If you're inactive, it'll help you move.

If I was asked what yoga has done for me, I would say that yoga has helped me identify and return to my true nature. It has taken me out of physical and mental pain and given me the support I was desperately looking for – be it a different form of support than I envisaged. Through my practice I've become physically stronger yet mentally calmer, which is quite a thing for someone who, in the past has been described as a person with A-type, Pitta or Red personality characteristics. Practising yoga helps me to constantly disentangle my thoughts and leaves me feeling more peaceful and a lot more accepting of 'what is'. My coach training alone didn't bring me that.

Nineteen years ago, my daughter was diagnosed with a serious chronic eye condition. Our GP told me to go home and not worry after I noticed her pupils were different sizes; he suggested I was overthinking and being an over anxious mother. I didn't agree, my intuition told me to get a second opinion. So, I booked an appointment with a local optician and from there we were sent straight to hospital. Her condition was explained as rare, hard to detect and serious. The abnormal cells in her eyes were confirmed as significant and if left untreated she would have lost her sight within months.

Eleanor was just six years old and Sebastian was four. I remember it clearly; I was driving past the city centre flyover in Leicester, when I turned to peer at the back seat to see my babies both fast asleep in their car seats, slumped at different angles. It was the start of a nineteen-year relationship with hospitals in Leicester, Nottingham and London. The consultant told us that we were going to get to know each other very well. Life turned upside down. As Ellie's condition developed and we were met with different scenarios, her condition always followed the more serious route. It felt like we were slipping into the unknown with no control whatsoever. For years we travelled twice a week to London to sit in a dimly lit waiting room for five hours at a time, before seeing a professor who would, over time, save our lovely girl from losing her sight altogether. We were worried, frustrated yet appreciative. We kept a record of all our hospital visits and only recently realised that we'd spent the equivalent of one whole year sitting in one particular waiting room.

During that time, I was also diagnosed with a serious spinal disease. Ellie's medications came with a lot of responsibility, as did her visits, so I was under a lot of stress and worry as any parent would be, along with the fear of my diagnosis. I remember the first time we drove to London together, just Ellie and myself. I had no idea where I was going or where I was going to park. All I knew, was that I needed to get her in front of the right people. Dean, my husband, had no other option than to keep showing up at work and keep the family finances under control. I threw all my attention into supporting our children and working when I could. My back pain was horrible most of the time; I wouldn't stand if I could sit, and I wouldn't sit if I could lay down. Whatever was happening to me was slowly getting worse and I felt silently depressed and miserable. I gained weight and felt untoned and unhealthy.

According to Yogic belief; we hold stress and tension in our hips and pelvis, manifesting as pain. I understand that now. Looking back, I was not only sitting for hours but also felt like I was carrying the weight of the world on my shoulders.

I wasn't earning much during those years. Its relative I understand, however, I was spending pretty much all the money I earned on petrol, parking and the underground. Dean was driving four hours every day to his job in Bradford and back with a reluctance to move further away from London and Sebastian was not spending time with us as he should have been and began to struggle at school. My baby girl was possibly losing her sight, my little boy was missing out and Finlay, our dog had to go into kennels during each visit because he was so boisterous. Our families and friends stopped offering to look after him, (understandably), which added to the cost and the logistics.

Looking back, they were tough times, those years nearly tipped me over the edge. My back, hip and neck pain continued, but I refused to cry, thinking I needed to deal with it, whatever. I didn't share or process my worries and I didn't acknowledge how I felt. I don't think I'd heard of the term 'self-love' or even 'wellbeing', they weren't common ways of being at that time or at least, I hadn't discovered them. I had private specialist appointments for my back which meant more time in hospitals, having lots of medical interventions, including wearing elasticated belts and painful spinal injections. I think I began to enjoy the attention, slipping into victim mode; passing all the responsibility for my 'health' onto my doctor which of course meant I wasn't taking responsibility for my emotional or spiritual health either.

Once I started to practice yoga, I became in control of something I thought I had no control over.

I started to enjoy the medical support I was experiencing; in fact, I was invited to take part in a free diabetes check on a dilapidated double-decker bus parked in a hospital car park. I felt as though I'd been to a spa for the day having spent hours having my blood pressure checked, giving blood and handing over urine samples. Believe me, when you confuse a health check on an old bus, sat in a car park with a spa day, you know you need help!

Strangely, my specialist doctor told me *not* to practice yoga. I was confused, especially as I had been a 1990's aerobics instructor and always in favour of *movement* with the belief 'use it or lose it'. With a seemingly valid explanation from my doctor and an excuse not to do much, I became increasingly comfortable with being a victim. I slept too much, which I believe was me aiming to disappear from my pain as well as the world, I struggled physically as well as mentally, and I continued to sit in my car, sit in waiting rooms, and sit on the sofa.

Sitting has recently been named 'the new smoking'. We sit at our breakfast table, sit in the car, sit at our desk, sit at the dining table, sit on the sofa and then go to bed! That's a lot of sitting. Sitting is said to be four times more compressive on the spine than standing and is increased even further by leaning forwards during computer work.

'Get a dog' my doctor had said. Dr 'O' was, and still is a respected doctor, and wasn't wrong in what he said, however he wasn't completely right either. I was told I had a horrible disease, frequent MRI scans confirmed it. I was told my disease was mild, but could eventually leave me seized up, yet at the same time, I was told I was hyper-mobile. I felt like my skeleton 'wobbled' instead of walked. I had the sensation of having two cocktail sticks poking into my sacroiliac joints, which were of course, inflamed. I felt like an insect made of two parts, that my spine would one day snap. I was told more than once *not* to practice yoga for fear of making myself even more mobile, and even more wobbly.

There are many different styles of yoga. Some physically demanding, some relaxing, some mostly standing and some mostly sitting. There are Yin styles and Yang styles. A Yin practice exercises the deep fascia, ligaments, tendons and joints of the body, whilst a Yang practice exercises the muscles. One is cool, one is warm. Finding the right style of yoga or asanas for you will be the difference between what's right for your body and mind and what isn't.
Not all styles of yoga suit everyone.

When I was twenty-one, I read a book entitled 'Feel the Fear and Do It Anyway' by Susan Jeffers. I don't remember too much about the content apart from the title. That book (at least it's title) has got me into all sorts of trouble over the years, but on this occasion it pointed me in the right direction. I was living in fear; fear of how I'd end up if things didn't get better. So, the rebel in me decided to try yoga anyway. Luckily, and unknowingly, I chose an Ashtanga style.

Ashtanga is a Yang style of yoga, the style of yoga I later became certified in. It's the most popular form of yoga in the western world boasting to strengthen muscles, increase flexibility, tone the body, and mobilise the joints. At first, those 'cocktail sticks' felt like hot needles but ever so slowly and over time the pain started to ease and lessen. I practised just once a week with a good and respected local teacher, Richard Voytak. I had no idea if it was going to help but I stopped believing in the expensive spinal injections I was having. They appeared to do nothing for me even though they had massive success rates on professional athletes from all over the world. Can you believe my private consultant even gave me free injections through his own frustration as the treatment didn't seem to be working? The injections were considered 'magical', and yet the magic didn't work for me, I was an anomaly.

Once recognised as chronic, my care moved to the NHS where I had full 1.5-hour spinal MRI scans every six months to measure the state, or decline, of my condition. I was told there was no cure. When the latest results arrived in the post, I had to sit down. It said there was no trace of Ankylosing Spondylitis or Sacroiliitis. What? This was after a year of practising yoga regularly.

I checked my name and address at the top of the letter. I re-read the letter several times. How could I have significant markers one minute, and not the next? How can repeated MRI scans present a disease, and then not? I was shocked. There are lots of variables I'm sure, maybe the disease burnt itself out? Maybe it stopped of its own accord? Maybe I didn't have a disease in the first place? Maybe I have it, but it just doesn't present itself any longer - who knows? I am HLA-B27 positive, which means I have a greater than average risk of developing certain autoimmune disorders. An autoimmune disorder is a condition that occurs when the immune system mistakenly attacks and destroy healthy body tissue. A genealogist told me that autoimmune disorders can, but don't necessarily pass down from parent to child but can cluster in families. This helped explain the possible connection between my daughter's Iritis condition and my own. The fantastic news was that I started practising yoga, and a year later the pain I had suffered on a daily basis stopped. The NHS weren't going to find out why or how my conditioned changed. Why would they? It was all the evidence I needed; practising yoga asanas became an integral part of my life. Fifteen years later the National Ankylosing Spondylitis Society (NASS) of Britain, recommends yoga to help relieve AS pain by improving range of movement, flexibility and promote ribcage expansion to improve breathing, whilst relieving stress and aiding relaxation.

Doctors at Moorfields Eye Hospital worked tirelessly, refusing to give up on Eleanor and save her from losing her sight altogether. It didn't go without heart-breaking statements to include one very logical but insensitive doctor telling her at the age of ten, that she needn't worry because when the day came, she would be able to choose which colour glass eyes she'd like, and rest assured that no one would know they weren't real. I remember asking her to kindly stop and told her we didn't need any further information thank you. Thankfully professor Peng Khaw's care and attention was outstanding, he, along with consultant John Brookes did and still do everything in their power to save her sight. There are no guarantees in life, but this created a profound effect on how I thought about everything. It gave me massive feelings of relief even though Ellie continues to have invasive treatments every day, week and month; it also gave me feelings of wanting to give back to society somehow. Her medication, treatment and operations had cost the NHS thousands of pounds and I became curious as to how I could help others.

A Safe Place

We'd spent many years traveling up and down the M1, and the short distance between Kings Cross and Old Street on the underground, and during that time I repeatedly noticed posters for Samaritans. Every week I was drawn to the same posters until I looked them up on the internet and decided to find out more. If I attended an open day, I might be chosen to train as a volunteer listener. I wouldn't get paid and maybe I'd have been better off working and saving for my pension, but I had a stronger urge to give back.

Being invited to a selection day was one of the most exhilarating, yet frightening things I've done. Not being familiar with a large corporate environment and modern way of selection, I was terrified. When my acceptance letter came through the post, I felt jubilant. I became one of twelve out of fifty people to train to become a listener from their small office in Grantham.

Many people are in a lot of pain when they call Samaritans. Some calls are short, some are long, lasting over an hour. Some people are angry, some quiet and unresponsive, some incredibly emotional and upset. I'm not sure if you can say you enjoy working for Samaritans, it's just something you do and hope to make a difference by being present and really listening to others' situations and emotions.

I felt engaged in the conversations but disliked the office. The chairs and the headrests made me feel sick as the room felt clean but dirty at the same time; there were two desks for two listeners and two phones. When a call comes in, the listener lets the phone ring three times before answering; that way the caller doesn't feel 'jumped upon'. Within the first minute we were trained to ask the caller if they felt suicidal, the caller will simply say 'no' if they're not, but if they do, there may be a chance the listener can help support them in that moment and help save their life, or to put it correctly, give them the autonomy to help themselves, and save their own life. Some callers may have already taken an overdose before calling, so time and efficiency in what appears to be a very personal question is paramount to the service they provide. Some callers may have lost their budgie, others have come out of relationships, lost a loved one or been abused. All callers are treated with the same respect whatever their reason for calling. I haven't personally called Samaritans for my own support but would be confident in their ability to support me.

Our mat can become our safe place, a place we can go, and a place we can be honest with who we are and what's going on in our lives. Being honest and vulnerable with ourselves helps us understand where we are in this moment.

I sat one relatively quiet evening in the office, reading a book from a pine bookshelf, at the back of the room. The book described a man's situation having been sent to prison after horrifically but accidentally knocking down a woman in his car. I forget the title. He arrived at a cell with three other inmates, he was frightened and naive. He tried to start a conversation by asking about the bucket in the corner of the room (clearly an old book).

'Is that where I take a p*ss?' he asked.

'Yes - if we let you' was the reply. It was his first experience of a long, painful and torturous time in prison.

Samaritans organisation also trains inmates as listeners, a selected few, who want to support others within the prison, go through a process the same as I had. They become listeners to their fellow inmates. Samaritans support people in the moment, supporting their needs in the here and now. I enjoyed the learning and experience and hope to have given back as intended.

Being a volunteer Samaritan as 'Amanda 3' for a year led me to invest in a two year training course to become an International

Coach Federation (ICF) accredited Personal Performance and Development Coach or simply put, a Life Coach (that was a mouthful!). I decided I wanted to build on my experience and help people move forwards. I was still enjoying hairdressing but became hugely interested in the subject of personal development and what it has to offer. A massive box arrived full of folders, books and DVD's along with dates for live lectures taking place just outside London. I took it to a small shed I had in the garden which had a desk, armchair and paintings hanging all around it. It was a shed I'd created to give me my own space in the sunshine. A place to sit, read and listen to the birds. I opened the box in nervous anticipation, as you do when you're about to embark on something outside of your comfort zone. It was one of those moments where you think, 'What have I done?' mixed with excitement for the new possibilities ahead. I was grateful for my time at Samaritans having spent four hours every other week, in the office, and I was a little sad to leave but happy to get away from the 'clean but dirty' headrests.

In the perfect world, I believe every woman should have a shed. It's a place to think, to be ourselves, to do whatever the hell we want.

Two years later and hours, upon hours of study, I became an accredited coach having qualified with three distinctions. Those distinctions were a big deal for me. I spent time with interesting and intellectual people from different professions and countries, I learned things I didn't know existed, I read book after book on self-development and revelled in it. Here, I'm going to share some of that learning with you.

The great thing about any book is that it waits for you, just like a yoga mat. It allows us to be in control of when and where we pick it up or roll it out.

The Bliss List

One day, whilst in the shower where all good ideas take place, I decided to simply write down all the words that made me feel good. I didn't know what I was going to do with them, but I continued all the same. I later named it 'My Bliss List' and it was the list that later led me to teaching yoga. My Bliss List, I suppose, was a simplification of what I had learnt. It was like a thesis at the end of an intense two-year training period and three years of experience in coaching others. Funny how the simplest things can become the pinnacle of ones learning and be most effective.

Your 'Bliss List' will help you re-engage with the fun and light-hearted side of your inner being and reconnect you with your urges, passions and purpose, those things that make you 'tick'. Instead of working from the outside in, it helps you work from the inside out. It reminded me of things I'd stopped enjoying and gave me a very clear path to follow.

Imagine this, a mixture of practising yoga with things on your Bliss List. You're enjoying each day, you're enjoying the good times and feel strong and resilient enough to ride whatever life throws your way. You wake up in the morning knowing there's always something to consider, to learn and to enjoy. You know that during your day you'll smile, probably laugh but appreciate that at times, you might need the space and time to feel sad. You're living an honest life, listening to yourself and your own needs, whilst making a difference within your family, your community and the world. Your soul feels nourished, happy and content. Physically, you feel strong and your body and heart feels open; you can move, lift, bend and stretch. You're aware of your thoughts and what you allow to repeat or reside in your mind. You worry less about your past and those who don't value or support you, instead, you focus on today and your future. You have appreciation and gratitude for what you have, and those around you. You're open, honest, real and authentic. You do no harm, but take no sh*t. You honour your personal boundaries and value your time. You're living your life alongside your own unique *bliss* whilst enjoying being who you're born to be. Your soul smiles and greatly approves.

I've been practising yoga for a few years now. As soon as I sit down on my mat, I feel engaged, I feel like I'm 'home'. I sit cross legged and do a little sway, and as soon as I do that, I'm in the zone. Notice what you do when you go to your mat. Maybe you sway too? I do hope so. Maybe you don't feel anything yet, but you will. Keep going to your mat.

A Bliss List is made up of things that make our hearts sing. It has nothing to do with ego or expectations which we too often get wrapped up in. It's a simple list; a very important list of things that make our face grin and our body do a little dance.

'We often feel tired. Not because we've done too much but because we've done too little of what sparks a light in us'.

A Bliss List is one of the most powerful tools I believe I can share with you. What will a Bliss List do for you?

- It'll help you indulge in your own life
- It'll help you re-engage in what makes you happy
- It'll remind you of things you've forgotten about
- It will help motivate you into doing things you enjoy
- It'll prevent you relying solely on others for direction
- It can pave the way to a forgotten passion
- It can lead a passion into a purpose
- It can support you if you feel restless or lost
- It can serve you for the rest of your life

Here's how to write your list; start writing down random words to describe things that make you feel happy, maybe odd words that don't make much sense but you like the activity, sight, sound, touch, smell or feel about them. Any word that stimulates or excites you. Write down words you like, for example my favourite word as a child was 'Pebble'. As a child I was going to grow up and live in 'Pebble Cottage', it hasn't happened yet but I'm happy to say it still could. I'm doing a little wiggle here as I write this; in the meantime, pebbles, be it in the back garden or on a beach, excite me.

Here are a few words from my Bliss List

Sheds	Vegan Food	Reading
Allotments	Forests	Sand
Allotment sheds	Fresh air	Sea
Baking	Gym clothes	Sewing
Balance	Hammocks	Silver birth trees
Bananas	Hats	Small spaces
Bare feet	House plants	Socks
Beach	Huts	Soup
Beach huts	Kevin Costner!	Sparkling water
Bed	Lavender	Stripes in the lawn
Bees	Lipstick	Sunsets
Bikes	Meeting new people	Sustainability
Birds	More Sheds	Swimming
Blankets	Movement	Transformation
Bookshelves	Music	Travel
Books	Nail Polish	Tree houses
Caravans	Napping	Trees
Canals	Notebooks	Tulips
Candles	Nutrition	Views
Clearings	Oats	Vintage
Colour	Olive trees	Walking
Creativity	Open spaces	Water
Cushions	Outdoor eating	Waves
Cutting hair	Painting	White flowers
Cycling	Pebbles	White walls
Dinner parties	Peanut butter	Wildlife
Dogs	Picnic	Windows
Fire Pits	Plants	Wood
Flip Flops	Poems	Wooden floors
Floating	Porridge	Words
Flowers	Puffa Jackets	Yoga

You might think these words obvious, however if you write your own list, you'll find yours are different. We might have similarities, but we will have similarities as humans. Keep coming back to your list and add a word, whenever you get the urge, don't wonder if that word is important or inclusive to you right now. Just keep writing them down. You're not looking for them to make any sense whatsoever. You're not looking for a solution either. Just keep adding your feel good words.

Note: This list was first created a while before I trained to be a yoga teacher. I was happily cutting hair, as I still am and offering life coaching sessions, but I was working too many hours without adding more of what makes me feel fulfilled. I didn't yet know what that looked like either. I knew I was looking for a feeling. A feeling of being connected with who I am, and I knew that once I got that feeling, I would have succeeded.

Think of things you've enjoyed throughout your life. Think about what you liked as a child. Our childhood interests are powerful secrets as to what makes us feel good before life got in the way. Maybe one-word flows to another completely different word; or maybe words associate with other words.

Making a Bliss List gives us a signpost and leads us when we need direction. It also gives us a platform for self-expression, it helps us to release our creativity and with that imagination, and innovation. Look at your list (Let it grow over time), dream about things on your list, play with them, and ask yourself why you wrote those words. The more we surround ourselves with actions, experiences and tangible objects from our list in any area of life, the happier we feel. They're just words to someone else but they're nuggets of happiness that can make an hour, a day, a month, a year or the rest of our life a more wonderful experience. My intention is to live alongside my Bliss for the rest of my life. In fact, I'll go as far as to say that I can't believe that years of learning personal development tools and strategies, funnelled into a simple list of words.

I could have bare feet sitting or lying down inside my shed with a medley of cushions and a selection of plants around me and I'd be in heaven. I could be on a course (one that takes my interest), online or otherwise; surrounded by books and completion dates and I'd be stimulated and happy. I could be in a open space, an office, studio or room, surrounded by paintings and wall hangings whilst creating or making something. It could be on a laptop or with a sewing machine or a cake mixer or a pair of scissors; whichever, I'd be joyous. I could be floating on the water in the rain wearing my big floppy hat and I'd be doing my thing.

The sentences above possibly don't do it for you, but they do for me! On the other hand, your sentences may do nothing for me, but they do *everything* for you! We're different and that's why it doesn't work asking others what our next move should be. They don't know. They don't know our *'words'*. You already know the answers, you just haven't thought about it or identified them. One of the intentions of a coach is to tell you what you already know, but have forgotten about.

By knowing and doing what we love, we inspire and awaken the hearts of ourselves as well as others

Jot your words down on these blank pages and keep this book (forever!) Powerful things happen when we write them down.

_____

_____

_____

_____

_____

_____

_____

_____

A Brief History of Yoga

The development of yoga can be traced back over five thousand years to the beginning of the Vedic period, and the writings of the Vedas which are considered among the oldest, if not the oldest, religious works in the world. The Vedas were a collection of religious texts containing rituals, songs and mantras used by the Vedic Priests known as Brahmans. The texts were written in Sanskrit literature, the oldest language in the world, and now only spoken in a few remote northern villages in India, and by university students studying it. Rishis, who are Saints, Sages and Brahmans, documented their practices and beliefs in what was named 'The Upanishads' which translates to 'sitting at the feet of a master'. Their existence suggests that information was taken from the Vedas and transformed into a new form of understanding. The Upanishads transferred the basis and principles of the Vedas into more practical and personal teachings.

Sanskrit is a liturgical language, meaning a holy language, found in the scriptures of Hinduism, Buddhism and Jainism to which yoga is most closely related. Many teachers use Sanskrit names to describe different postures during a class. This makes yoga classes internationally understood. Most postures have one or two westernised names alongside a Sanskrit name.

The Upanishads were composed over several centuries and in over 200 scriptures, they reflect a strong need to express and communicate the deep mystical states and spiritual observations that the ancient yogis experienced.

At that time, it was suggested yoga was a mish-mash of ideas that often clashed or contradicted itself. The first systematic presentation of yoga came from Patanjali's Yoga Sutras. The dates these were compiled seem to be different depending where you look, but were believed to be written around two thousand years ago. All styles of yoga originate from Patanjali to include styles you might be familiar with such as Hatha,

Ashtanga, Kundalini, Vinyasa or Iyengar to name a few. According to my teachers in India it isn't known if Patanjali was male or female, one person or a group of people. That said, Patanjali is often referred to as 'he'. Patanjali's Yoga Sutras are made up of a collection of 196 Aphorisms or 'threads' referring to rules on the theory and practice of yoga.

The child in me is thrilled as yoga is often symbolised using an illustration of a tree. A living entity with roots, a trunk, branches, blossoms, and fruit, with eight separate branches suggesting different ways of living and being.

According to Patanjali's Yoga Sutras, there is an eight-fold path leading to liberation known as the 'Eight Limbs of Yoga'. The Sanskrit word 'Ashta' means 'eight' and 'anga' means 'limb'.

Yoga was passed down from the Vedas to the Upanishads, then to Patanjali before spreading far and wide travelling from one guru to another. In the 1950's two men became well known within the modern world of yoga. Sri Pattabhi Jois and B.K.S. Iyengar. Iyengar became known for his slow-paced form of yoga which is said to be good for beginners and those with specific physical restrictions, as this style uses many props to include chairs, blocks, bolsters and straps, in fact, anything to help achieve poses in a safe way.

I have only been to one Iyengar yoga class but thoroughly enjoyed it. It was in a village hall in Cornwall and it made us smile as the whole room was filled with apparatus to include chairs, many blocks and straps. We weren't sure what we were letting ourselves in for. Most of the women were over sixty-five and it was a two-hour class that was one of the slowest but hardest classes I've attended. Everyone in the room finished the class in a headstand. Ellie and I were incredibly impressed by the strength in the room that day and also their commitment to the practice. Iyengar teachers are very well trained and very detailed in their teaching, it is a great choice if you want a slow, safe and supported practice.

Sri Pattabhi Jois, along with B.K.S. Iyengar, were both taught by Tirumalai Krishnamacharya and are both known for bringing yoga to the western world. Sri Pattabhi Jois is also known for creating the six 'Series of Ashtanga Yoga' which in turn made the practice much more understandable as it became systematised. He opened a school of Ashtanga Yoga in Mysore, India in 1948. According to Patanjali and the Yoga Sutras there is an eight fold path leading to liberation known as the Ashtanga Yoga system or eight limbs of yoga.

Anyone wanting to learn under the guidance of Sri Patabhi Jois was recommended to start at the third limb which is the physicality of yoga known as 'asana'. Most people starting their yoga journey start there anyway, not realising there are eight limbs to yoga, and there are two limbs before asana.

The first of the eight limbs is called, The Yamas. The second limb, The Niyamas. Within the Yamas and Niyamas are five key principles or ways of living. B.K.S. Iyengar describes the Yamas and Niyamas as the 'golden keys to unlock the spiritual gates', transforming each action into one that originates from a deeper and more connected place within ourselves. The Yamas and Niyamas are suggestions to help support our lives and ways of behaving, whether we consider ourselves spiritual or not.

Is it a load of nonsense? Well, you tell me, that decision must lie with you, your own beliefs and what you want to believe.

I believe in yoga; I'm also conscious of not wanting to be a 'yoga bore' to my friends and family. I suppose we all have a level we're prepared to go, however, the more I've learned the more fascinated I am and the more 'on board' I become. How could people have known so much, so long ago? I have a sneaky suspicion that at some time during the past, a smart savvy individual learned the principles of yoga, took it back to the West, changed the language and wrapped it up in 'fancy paper' and then sold it to the world as something new, naming it *personal development.*

A Journey to Yoga

My coach training taught me many things, but something that stands out was the learning around values and beliefs. Our values are what we learn from our parents, family, teachers and community, they're influenced by our country leaders, religions and traditions, we grow up with them, defend them and seldom challenge them. Values are our *rules* and *standards and part of our ego* that we unconsciously uphold. Values aren't easy to change and are the reason why we disagree or fall out with others. Our opinions stem from our beliefs based on our values and tend to be much more verbal! We have opinions based on what we believe to be right and true.

If a new way of thinking or behaving comes to the forefront we can be forgiven for thinking its mad, crazy or a waste of time. Why? Because it isn't our normal way of thinking or behaving. Our beliefs might tell us this is crazy based on our unconscious value behind it. Alternatively, maybe we're not curious enough to consider another way.

Here's a rather crude way of thinking about beliefs; Imagine you go out for a walk and slip over in the mud, leaving your hands dirty. Are you happy to wipe them with a tissue from your pocket or would you rather wash them with fresh water? Why is it then; for many westerners we feel that wiping our bottoms with dry toilet paper is correct and clean and yet many believe that those in other countries are dirty for washing themselves with water?

Learning about values and beliefs has helped me understand people's opinions, and with that I aim not to judge others, based on their beliefs. We all have options based on our values and because our values are our rules and standards; learning something new and acting upon it can be anything from difficult to stimulating.

The very first Yama is named Ahimsa. Himsa means violence or to cause harm. 'A' means not. So 'A-himsa' means no violence or not to cause harm. Ahimsa is ranked the highest and is the foundation upon which all other philosophical practices sit.

Reading that book in the office in Grantham made me feel physically sick. If everyone in the world made a pledge not to be violent to others (or ourselves), what a wonderful world we'd all live in. I think we can all relate to Ahimsa; inflicting physical or emotional violence or harm on others or others inflicting physical or emotional violence or harm on us, and what about the physical or emotional violence or harm we inflict on ourselves? I now find myself so attuned to this first and very powerful Yama that I find myself encouraging flies to escape from their prison behind glass, helping them escape through an open window. As they fly away, I hear myself saying 'Enjoy your life - be kind'.

Here's to rolling out our mats, to living an authentic and peaceful life, to laughing in the face of adversity and enjoying a little bit of bliss each and every day.

'Take no sh*t but do no harm, and practice yoga'

I sat in a cafe pre yoga teacher training telling a fellow yogi, who had recently qualified herself that I was going to book my YTT course as I was really interested in the 'Seven Arms of Ashtanga Yoga'. After falling off her chair with laughter she corrected me. 'It's the *Eight Limbs of Ashtanga Yoga,* are you sure you want to train to be a teacher?' It was funny and I'm the first to laugh at myself, but her judgement and enjoyment of my mistake triggered my 'inside voice', that sneaky voice that steps in, and told me I wasn't good enough. She was chuckling away at my expense and all I wanted to say was 'Oh boll*cks to you'.

We're often emotionally triggered by what others say or do, even if they say it in jest or ignorance. We can absorb their statement or mocking, or we can believe in ourselves and our own flawed perfection and do what we intend to do, regardless.

'I will not let anyone walk through my mind with their dirty feet'
– Gandhi

Twenty-six years ago, I taught aerobics. When I decided to stop teaching, I explained to my aerobics students that 'If I was ever to teach again, I would train to be a yoga teacher'. 'A yoga teacher?' They didn't understand, yoga was something only weirdos did. Life got busy and the years passed, and I forgot about that declaration.

Two months after stepping out of that café, I flew to India to live and breathe Ashtanga Yoga for five weeks and embrace those 'Seven Arms'. Go Mand!

Practising yoga asanas affects our minds as well as our bodies minus the endless pounding on our joints

I remember whilst being an aerobics teacher, going into a local health food shop. I got talking to the very knowledgeable shopkeeper whose name was Mrs Thorpe. I was twenty seven, slim and strong and had what could be described as an impressive 'four pack'. I wore crop tops, leggings and white trainers, and felt as fit as a flea as I ran up the steps into the shop.

We got into a conversation and I'm not sure what exactly we were talking about but I remember her suggesting that I look at all aspects of health and pointed out that my physical health, be it that I looked strong, fit and healthy was only one element of health. She reminded me that along with physical health we need nutritional, mental, spiritual, social and intellectual health. It was what I needed to hear, and I'm forever grateful for her wisdom and knowledge in that moment.

Fitness is the ability to perform athletic activity.
Health however is defined as 'the state where all the systems
of the body - nervous, muscular, skeletal, circulatory,
digestive, lymphatic, hormonal etc., are working to an optimal
level. A common mistake is that many of us think that physical
fitness equals health, but the truth is;
health has different facets.

Maybe you've tried yoga, maybe you haven't? From the feedback I get and what I can remember from my own learning; this is pretty much how the first few experiences of a yoga class go.

We try our first class; we get a bit lost, but by the end we feel OK. We tell the teacher - or think it in your head - that it was good and that we actually found it easier than we expected (apart from going into standing poses when we bring our foot from a Downward Facing Dog to between our hands!) We go to our second class and feel far more relaxed because we know what the room looks like and we realise that eating too near the start of the class is a bad idea – especially vegetable soup! We go to our third class, and feel like we've nailed it! The fourth class we realise we haven't nailed it at all, and that we need to breathe. That's when it feels like we're learning to drive again. (Pedals, gears and switches). The fifth time we become aware of our foot and hand placement but secretly want to be like some of the yogis at the front. The sixth time we start to notice there's so much to think about and we don't have the mental capacity to stare at the front row after all. We realise we were kidding ourselves that first day when we thought it was easy. And so, it goes on.

After the first year of practicing yoga (Ashtanga in this instance), we realise this really is a *practice* and that we never actually get to where we think or would like to be. After all, it's a thirty-year practice. Yoga always gives us somewhere to go, whatever our ability, capability or knowledge. At the same time, we begin to realise we don't have to reach daily or weekly goals and that today is the only place we need to be. Life lessons can come from our yoga training.

1. We're all different and on our own path or journey.
2. There is always somewhere to go, irrelevant of how accomplished we become.
3. We learn to accept what we can't change, either on or off our mats

We're perfectly imperfect right where we are today, look at the word imperfect; I'm-perfect.

Ancient Indian philosophy states that an individual is represented by different layers known as sheaths, that enclose the individual's self. Imagine we've arrived at this science covered in brown crispy leaves. Imagine those dry crispy leaves to be those of an onion; representing our ego. Our ego protects us, and will fight hard to allow us to do, say, and think, in a certain way, preventing us from looking less than we want to appear. As we begin to trust the process of yoga, the layers start to come away. Over time we work deeper towards the centre of our being, peeling back the layers, named *Koshas*. In turn, we become less of who we think we are, and more of who we really are.

The five Koshas:
Physical: Our body nourished by food.
Energetic: Energy. The life force of body and mind.
Mental: Our thoughts, emotions and feelings.
Intuitive: Knowledge, wisdom and awareness.
Bliss: Happiness, joy and love.

Ahamkara is the Sanskrit word for ego or a sense of "I-ness". Consciousness is when we become aware of ourselves, our surroundings and how we feel in the moment.

We can let go of our ego by practising forgiveness and appreciation, being honest, being open, putting down our need to control, as well as our self-importance. Enjoying silent moments alone and becoming more aware of the journey to the centre of our being, knowing it may take months or years but trusting in the process. In my experience, through the practice of yoga, the layers come away when they're ready, they fall away naturally and smoothly. Yoga feels soft and right and trusting. When we're in a position of trust, we tend to cope with the timing and the lessons, and as we continue our practice, we improve our patience, whilst embracing mindfulness, humbleness, and wisdom.

A Yoga Shala is the name given to 'a place of yoga'
where practitioners go to practice, learn, and grow.
Many yoga businesses use the word Shala in their name.
I practice and film from my shed in the garden,
It's my 'Shedquarters' and 'Shed-Shala'.

Prana vs Chi

Yoga asanas distribute Prana, or Chi known as subtle energy. Chi is the Chinese name, and Prana is the Indian name for energy; the energy that flows through us and everything around us. This energy mediates between the physical and emotional aspects of self. Yoga teaches us to control this energy.

The western world of medicine has historically been intrigued with the skeleton and organs. Practices have historically cut through the connective tissue to get to the bones and organs within. It is believed in Eastern medicine, specifically both the Indians and Chinese, put their attention on the connective tissue and believe that within our connective tissue is energy or life force. This life force travels around the body via thousands of *Nadis* or *Meridians* connecting and corresponding with our nervous, endocrine and other bodily systems. The words Nadi and Meridian have the same or similar meaning; again, just different words from different countries and philosophies. These pathways of energy intertwine between organs, muscles, bone, fascia and joints. Neither Prana or Chi or anything equivalent can be found in westernised medical journals. Asana (yoga postures) and Breath, according to yogic belief, are different ways to control and feel the energy within us.

Chinese Yin philosophy appears to offer more information on the Meridians and the transportation of energy through the body and the Indian Yang philosophy appears to offer more information on the seven Chakras or epicentres and main energy centres.

The main meeting points for our body's energy are called the 'Chakras' of which there are seven.
Chakra also means 'wheel'.

The seven Chakras start from the base of our spines and finish above the top of our heads. When the Chakras or vortexes of energy are stimulated, they are said to 'spin'. We aim to awaken and spin our Chakra wheels allowing them to open and exchange energy with one another as they aim to maintain a balanced system.

It is yogic belief that Chakras can reflect where we are at any given time. For me, it doesn't matter if you believe in the Chakras or not, I believe they provide information and increase self-awareness to enable us to nurture our minds, body and spirit so that we feel more whole as human beings.

Different poses can affect Chakras because of how they are able to change and direct energy in the body.

Each Chakras is attached to a colour of the rainbow, a location in the body, a sound, a sense, a psychological function, a zodiac, a celestial body and a crystal or stone. It's up to us how far we want to understand the Chakras and what heightened knowledge associated with them can do for us. Not only do asanas (Yoga poses) stimulate the Chakras, but also other natural factors create shifts in our energy or 'vibration'. Visualisations, eating foods of certain colour or constituents, wearing certain colours, working with crystals from the earth, chanting, and connecting with nature.

The ancient Chakra belief system didn't appear to show there were colours, identifying them as colourless; there is also no mention of 'Chakra colours' in the Upanishads; the secret and sacred knowledge texts from which the Chakras came. A colour, however, gives them an association and helps us remember them better. For me, this proves there is no absolute information, and that we must continue in our quest for our own truth, through our own perception and discernment.

Colours are something we can remember and identify easily, bringing a sense of universal language. Using colour in the wheels of Chakra helps us collectively understand, as well as be understood. Learning where we lack energy helps us learn about our personal behaviours and triggers leading to our own personal growth and a positive future.

Chakra colours are the same as a rainbow, a spectrum of light in a band of familiar colours; red, orange, yellow, green, blue, indigo and violet. The words *'Richard of York Gave Battle In Vain'* is a schooldays association and easy way to remember the colour of the rainbow and energy balancing Chakras.

Sir Isaac Newton in the 17th century wanted to make the intermingled colours of the rainbow more understandable. If he separated the many colours, they could be given colour names. Originally, he identified five colours but later, indigo and violet were added due to the work of Pythagoreans and their will to create connections between colour and sound being the number seven. How crazy is that?

Here are the seven Chakras and their position in the body. Later on, we'll revisit them and put them to work for our own personal practice and advantage. When we feel good, our world keeps getting better.

Muladhara is our base Chakra and located at the base of our spines, at the perineum.
Svadhisthana is located in the lower abdomen, womb, genitals and sacrum.

Manipura is located above the navel and behind the stomach.

Anahata is located at the sternum.

Vishuddha is located in the throat.

Ajna is located at our 'Third Eye'.

Sahasrara is located at the crown or top of our head.

Golden Triangle

My first trip to Delhi, Jaipur and Agra was in April 2016. Dean and I travelled to India to experience what is referred to as the Golden Triangle. We took three weeks off work and planned the trip ourselves, wanting to experience people and situations personally, rather than be part of a tour or guided trip. I asked almost every Indian I had the opportunity to speak to, if they practised yoga. They all said they did, with a big smile and some with a pleasing and peaceful wobble of their head. I later learned, this 'wobble' of the head translates to 'acceptance'.

I try not to judge, however I didn't believe that many who said they practised yoga actually did, until one very polite tuk-tuk driver from Jaipur informed me that we don't have to practice the physical form of yoga to *practice* yoga. The physical form as I've mentioned is only one element of yoga, the third of eight limbs.

A man who practices yoga is termed as a Yogi
A woman who practices yoga is termed as a Yogini

The first four limbs of yoga attach to our outer being, our way of behaving, our attitudes and actions. The last four limbs of yoga attach to our inner being and concentrate on our minds.

I didn't take much notice of the other seven limbs when I first qualified as an instructor. In fact, I was much more excited by the outer physical practice over what was happening any deeper. Of course, this was my choice. You can practice yoga as an exercise only and many do, however, over time, my curiosity returned, and I started to embrace the other limbs. You could say my 'onion' was starting to peel, and underneath my outer layers I began to feel there was so much more to me, behind my ego. I could sense I was letting go of some of the limitations and insecurities that had kept me 'imprisoned' in life, without even realising it. I learned I didn't have to share anything with others either, which is so non-coach-like as coaching is a talking therapy. I became aware that it was just me, with my body and my mind on my mat; moving, breathing, meditating. All I had to do was show up, everything I had learned during my personal development training was happening anyway, the only difference, was that I could make sense of it and put it into context; others might not know what that context is, but it doesn't matter, you still gain the same results. For me it was exciting and intriguing. What I'm aiming to say here is you get what you need without having to intellectualise the process. It just happens, like magic!

Am I confusing you? I hope not.
I'm going to call it quiet confidence.

As we travel along the path of The Eight Limbs of Yoga our consciousness becomes stronger and our minds become calmer and clearer. We grow what can be described as 'quiet confidence', where we learn to let go, feel more connected, trust in the moment and are far less flustered by day-to-day events.

Mindfulness or consciousness is something that, in my opinion, we have lost or forgotten about due to living somewhat superficial and egotistical lives. We're too busy looking outwards searching and blaming instead of feeling inwards. We're too busy looking at what we need or want rather than enjoying what we already have. We aim to look good by others viewing our lives (social media really hasn't helped). I, along with many, was spending a lot of time putting my attention on searching and looking *outside* instead of noticing what's really going on *inside*. My answers come to me far easier now. Looking out allows others to influence us. When we hide behind our outer layers or ego, it leads us to say and do things that don't serve the authentic human we are and were born to be.

When we practice our postures, it helps if we change our thoughts into feelings. This allows us to connect to the inside or internal being. When we listen to our bodies and feel our way, our bodies can tell us what we're holding onto both physically and mentally. When we mentally let go, we create space. Space allows new and fresh thoughts, ideas and ways of living to the forefront of our minds. My first 'downward facing dog' ignites the start of my body warming up and my mind letting go. Try 'walking your dog', practice walking away from your daily worries or troubles.

Part Two

The First Limb of Yoga
The Five Yamas

1st
Ahimsa
Non-Violence

- Self-love
- Compassion
- Understanding
- Support

The five Yamas are within the first Limb in Patanjali's Eight Limbed Path of Yoga. They're considered 'restraints' and in simple terms; things *not to do.*

Ahimsa is the first Yama and means non-violence to ourselves, others or any living thing on the planet. The Yoga Sutras tell us that Ahimsa should form the foundation upon which all other philosophical practices are built. Non-violence can be practised by the way we physically treat ourselves, and others; the way we speak to ourselves and others. It can be our attitudes towards our diet, how we feel about fear and courage and how we demonstrate compassion. It can be practised at home, at work, during leisure and of course during our time on our mat.

Fear plays a big part in Ahimsa, as fear can lead to insecurity, control, greed, aggression and violence. If our ego is inflated, we will constantly want more; as we fear we never have enough. If we believe we don't have enough, we're likely to become frustrated and possibly angry. Fear can lead us to aggression in our quest to regain *control.* If we feel insecure, we may also become angry and again lead us to *himsa* or violence (spoken or otherwise). Fear can be an instinctual part of our survival. Feeling fear can motivate us to fight, or run in the opposite direction.

However, fear can also be part of our imagination, as we build pictures in our minds and create outcomes that haven't happened and may not happen. It helps if we can differentiate between the real and imaginary. The acronym of F.E.A.R (**F**alse **E**vidence **A**ppearing **R**eal) helps us question if our imagination is the creator of our fears.

Is it false or is it real?

Balancing our 'What if's?' with our sense of certainty, can be practised on our mats alongside helping us engage with our feelings and emotions, giving us the opportunity to slow down, take stock and weigh up our choices.

Our physical yoga practice can help us face our fears during poses that require an element of risk. They may not work, and we might fall over or even injure ourselves. I'm not suggesting we injure ourselves here however, whilst on our mat we can weigh up the pros and cons of taking risks, in turn we become a little more courageous. Courage is not the absence of fear but the ability to put fear to one side. Putting a cushion on the floor when practising crow for instance, allows us to be courageous working alongside fear, but also softens the fall if we do. Same applies for using a wall for headstands and handstands. We don't have to be *all in* when wanting to be courageous and we don't have to be *all out* when faced with risk.

'What would you do if you weren't afraid?'

If, or when, people and situations frustrate us, we often lose our compassion; we turn the other way refusing to notice their story, situation or message. Sympathy, empathy, understanding, care and concern all sit alongside compassion. When we feel compassion for others, we come into a place of non-harming. If we look at these situations positively, we realise that others can help us learn and grow. It's important also that we find compassion for ourselves. I sometimes get on my own nerves, so spending time giving myself sympathy, empathy and understanding brings me to a place of self-care and self-love.

Self-love wasn't something that was spoken about years ago, however, we hear it a lot now. It's OK to look after yourself. It's OK to put yourself first. It's OK to listen to what our own bodies, minds and souls need. Think of yourself as your own child within. What does that child need? How can we *nourish* ourselves? How can we *feed* ourselves? Maybe we'll all have different ideas on what that looks like but for me, time on my mat, whilst practising slowly and mindfully with moments spent literally hugging myself has been a dreamy and lovely way to love myself. Sometimes doing this makes me feel sad as emotions come to the surface, but that's a good thing, as they were there anyway, I can then let go and release them. Mentally I ask myself to let go of worries, to let go of my fears, and to forgive others and myself, which all help ease my frustrations.

'If your compassion does not include yourself.
It is incomplete'
- Buddha

A good reminder to not push too hard into poses or practice when we don't feel well is practising Ahimsa. I have a tender right shoulder; ahimsa reminds me to back off during a physically demanding practice or avoid asanas that need the strength of that shoulder. When we practice physical asanas from a place of non-violence our practice becomes wiser and more sustainable.

Are you listening to your body's needs in a loving and caring manner?
Are you giving yourself time to stop and reflect?
Are you giving your mind space to allow your Bliss to enter?
Are you nourishing your body with what you consume?
Are you treating others how you'd like to be treated yourself?
Are you giving yourself the same love and compassion you give others?

A dynamic practice is physically demanding and a complete contrast to a Yin or 'restorative' practice. Asking, instead of telling yourself what you need, is using Ahimsa.

2nd
Satya
Truthfulness

- Authenticity
- Being real instead of nice
- Speaking with clarity and courage

Satya is the second Yama. When we think of truthfulness you may agree that our mind leads us to thoughts of fibs or lies. Lies we tell others and lies others tell us. Our minds may have already remembered a situation where someone deceived us through untruths or actions they made. We may be reminded of a time when we told ourselves something that wasn't true, because it was less painful than knowing and accepting the truth. I am the Queen of this.

We have no control over what others do to us, but we have every bit of control over what we do to others, and ourselves. We tell ourselves untruths, we tell ourselves stories; we reside with beliefs and opinions based on our values, that create imaginary situations in the hope that we can manipulate life into the way we want it.

The question is, *are we being true to ourselves,* or are we telling ourselves incorrect stories or even fairy tales? A tougher question is, *who are we without those stories?* What will we do if we stop believing that untruth or fairy-tale? It can leave us feeling vulnerable but on the other hand it can take us back to 'base' where we can begin to grow, learn and develop and live a more authentic life. When we tell ourselves stories it's often because we're in fear of our own truth. Instead we choose to hide behind our ego.

Going to our mats allows us to be completely open and vulnerable. It allows us to be honest and say it like it is. We can cry like a baby if that's what it takes, knowing we have the opportunity to be truthful in our minds, and hearts. This is uncomfortable but it allows us to rise from the ashes bit by bit, day by day, growing stronger whilst leaving our distorted stories behind. We're aiming to be the most honest and truthful version of ourselves.

What we don't want, is to find ourselves in a room one day with everyone we know; and not know who we are, what we stand for, or which version of ourselves to be.

Carl Jung, a Swiss psychologist born in 1875, shared four theories to include our self, persona, shadow and anima/animus.

Jung recognised that we present an exaggerated version of ourselves, our 'persona', to others to help us leave an impression. It may not be the same character we display most when we're alone or at home. His theory suggests that when we're seen, we wear a 'mask'. That mask is our alter ego.

Here's an example:

A yogi may want to express a particular persona to the outside world, one that implies they have it all together; that they are calm and maybe a little serene, that they have a good nature and never has a negative thought, emotion or action. But that same yogi may be throwing every pot and pan out of the cupboard in temper, when alone at home. That yogi could be paddling like crazy to maintain a persona that suits their alter ego.

The question is, what effect is that having on that person, that human being? What actions, stories and untruths do we create to prop us up in our aim to continue? We serve ourselves better if we're real with others and honest with ourselves, rather than aiming to believe or be something untrue.

Our 'shadow' is another part of our personality that lives within us. It's the part of us that we don't want to share with others. Others might see that shadow, but we will do everything we can to push it away, refuse and deny it.

Supposing we personify that shadow and imagine it to be a person living inside of us, they have been there all our life. Imagine that person standing in front of you, and maybe even give that person a name. I call mine Madge (I know, funny)

See that person who's taking all the strain of your persona and ego. How are they looking? Would it be fair to say that this person inside of you is stressed, tired, or overworked? Take another look; would it be fair to say that you've created a lot of lies and stories to the outside world but poor old *Madge* is having to carry the truth day in and day out? Is Madge OK? Is Madge coping? Can Madge continue to take the responsibility that you put on her day after day, week after week, month after month or even year after year? *Is your shadow exhausted?*

If your shadow could speak it may ask for empathy. It may ask you to show your heart. It may want you to sit and listen so that it can cast off the load it carries. Most of your lives together you've been stressing your shadow and asking the impossible. Asking it to perform beyond any human capability. If you sit long enough and listen, your shadow can tell you what's wrong. It can talk to you in a truthful, honest and open way, all you need to do is identify that you have a shadow and listen to it.

But what if you don't want to listen to your shadow? If we choose not to listen, then our shadow will continue to carry the load we put upon it and in time it will suffer whatever consequences may come of denying it.

Allowing our shadow to tell us what's wrong allows us to unpack our emotions and highlight what we need. Once we know what we need, we can choose to do something about it.

My shadow tells me that love can come from me and that I don't need to chase it. That I mustn't work too long or too hard. That I can't do everything, and I deserve time off to rest. That I don't have to be strong for other people all the time and that it's totally acceptable to focus on myself and my own needs first. My shadow reminds me that it's a good thing to give myself time to 'cry' even though actual tears rarely show up. I get caught up in efficiency and its O.K. to wait until another time or another day. My shadow tells me it's not always food I want but a hug or a conversation or a long hot bath. Being kind, thoughtful and realistic to my shadow has changed the way I treat myself.

If we go back to the meaning of yoga, we remind ourselves that it can also mean separation or disentanglement. The thing we're aiming to disentangle from, is whatever it is that's stopping us feeling free. Yoga helps to liberate us; it brings us to a place of balance and independence.

Going to our mats regularly with an honest and truthful heart allows us to listen to what's really going on. Opening the body through asanas releases our innermost and privately guarded emotions, worries, frustrations, and secrets. By releasing these trapped emotions, we invite a new way of being to the forefront, without even having to tell another living soul. We're aiming for Moksha, meaning freedom. Over time we feel lighter and brighter, helping us psychologically 'get out of jail'.

I knew I wanted to be a yoga teacher and I wanted to throw myself in. I wanted to travel somewhere with a different culture, meet local people and come away with new learnings. I chose a place where I'd stay in a little shed with hammocks, tall trees, sand and a warm sea; where I could be quiet and study. I wanted to live, breathe and learn from its place of origin, so I chose to go back to India, and felt completely aligned, having been truthful with myself and what I wanted to achieve.

Sometimes we need to tell a little lie, to save the feelings of others. At these times Satya asks us to be truthful but also reminds us to be kind.

In 2008 we went to Cairo, our travel guide, Mustafa, offered his services for a second day. We'd already been to the pyramids, Cairo Museum, the markets, a couple of Mosques, perfumeries and too many rug shops. We got on well with Mustafa, he was an intelligent man in his mid-twenties, who spoke seven languages and aimed for success in life, he was impressing us with the names of many more places we could experience with him. However, I asked him if we could spend a day meeting a few local people, to understand more about everyday Egyptian life. I asked him if we could visit the village he grew up in, meet his friends, have a cup of tea with his mother and father maybe (the cheek!) He said he'd never been asked such things and he'd think about it. Two days later, he picked us up early in the morning taking us to a dressmaker where Ellie and I were adequately covered and presented for the day, which meant purchasing a jellabiya, a long traditional dress and headscarf to cover our hair. We met his friends and their family, who lived in a house with forty goats residing in the rooms on the first floor of their house, we went to his village where he told us people had never seen green and blue eyes; we visited his parents who lived in an immaculately presented flat situated along a dilapidated road with huge intermittent piles of litter and large puddles of still, stagnant water.

'Do you like Egypt?' we were asked.

'Oh yes, we love Egypt' we replied, nodding enthusiastically.

We sat in a large circle with Mustafa's mother, father, and two brothers. They made us tea and offered us cake. It was an extraordinary and wonderful experience but with many long silences.

'Do you like Egyptian actors?' we were asked. (Hmm, Egyptian actors?)

'Oh yes - Omar Sharif, Doctor Zhivago', replied Dean, as I felt rescued in the moment. Big smiles all around followed by another long silence.

'What about Egyptian food? You like Egyptian food?'

I wanted to fall to the floor with laughter or maybe hysteria as we were advised to stay away from the food altogether instead, sticking with the hotel food and fast food services. I wanted to say, 'The Fillet-O-Fish with large fries is outstanding and only one Egyptian pound at the moment,' but of course I didn't. I told them what they wanted to hear. 'The Egyptian food is delicious, especially the Baba Ganoush' I said - Phew!

Bringing truthfulness to our practice allows us to step away from our ego. We become honest in our movements which makes us far less likely to injure ourselves. We become more transparent during our meditations which gives us an authentic platform to expand.

If we do tell a fib, lie or untruth, Satya reminds us to do the right thing, sooner rather than later. It's often our ego that doesn't want us to apologise. Our shadow is a lot happier when we come from a place of honesty and sincerity. People who are truthful, gain more respect - wouldn't you agree?

'Does my bum look big in this?'
This is an example of exemption.
'No'

Why fib? Because sometimes the truth can hurt.
(Ahimsa - non harming)

3rd

Asteya
Non-Stealing

- Stealing from others
- Stealing from the world
- Stealing ideas
- Stealing the limelight
- Stealing from our grandchildren

Asteya literally means non-stealing, 'steya' means to steal, putting an 'A' at the front of the word means *not* to steal. Asteya is the third Yama within the first of eight limbs of yoga. It is the abandonment of the intent or desire to possess or steal anything whether it is material, a relationship, time, energy, or a natural resource. Anything to which does not belong to us.

I was in my last year of infant school. I must have been ten or eleven and I'd talked my mother into buying me a pair of ridiculously high black wedge shoes, I can see them now. She said I wouldn't be able to walk in them, but I assured her repeatedly, whilst walking up and down the carpeted shop floor that I could. The next day, I turned left outside my house to visit a friend named Wendy. It was the perfect opportunity to show off the 'new me' before the beginning of term the following Monday. By the time I got to the second lamp post I realised my mother was right. Walking uphill was slightly easier as the wedge of the shoe created a level ground, however, walking downhill was impossible. Even though it was so long ago, I can remember the discomfort and stress I was putting on my back and knees, deciding though that the irritation was secondary to looking like a glorious teenager! I arrived at Wendy's bungalow without the need to cross a road and was welcomed by her parents and invited into her bedroom. Wendy was sitting on her bed and there, on her dressing table right in front of me, was a pair of earrings I'd bought the week before. I couldn't believe it!

I couldn't talk. I just stared at them. A pair of gold (coloured) hoop earrings. How could she? How could my friend take something that wasn't hers? I remember it like it was yesterday.

'They're my earrings!' I exclaimed 'Did you take my earrings?' I was shocked and angry! Wendy was nonchalant and didn't deny it. I've never forgotten that first experience of having something taken from me. It upset me greatly; I instantly detached myself from my friendship with Wendy, said goodbye to her parents and walked out of the door, choosing instead, to direct all my attention on trying to walk upright.

Wearing high heels is supposed to make a woman look more attractive by making us appear more sexual. Wearing heels tilts the pelvis and it increases vertical motion at the hip and creates shorter strides. Pressure is also put on the back, knees and joints. Wearing heels can make our backs ache along with our feet. Walking on the balls of our feet also shifts our centre of gravity forward, forcing us to arch our backs. A youthful body is more likely to tolerate this but as we get older, we jeopardise our physical health

Why is it that some memories hang round? Why are some so easy to recall? Why is it that some memories, the ones we don't enjoy or upset us, aren't easy to forget?

As humans, we grow up to experience lots of 'firsts' during the first seven to ten years of life, and with that, a whole bunch of emotions. Having my earrings stolen was a *first* for me. Should I experience something else getting stolen, my brain will remember that first experience and possibly endorse the feelings that came with it. I have lots of memories of that day. I can see Wendy sitting on her bed, her room, her curtains, my earrings and the apple trees outside her window.

Sir Francis Galton (1822-1911) was a half-cousin of Charles Darwin and the founder of psychometrics. He was the first to document the power of association to aid our memories and recall. Our memory works by associating everything we see, hear, feel, taste and smell, with a previous experience based on similar association. This is a natural way for our brains to link and connect everything we've ever known with any new information. The stronger the sensory associations, the better our ability to accurately recall the events, be them positive or negative.

The acronym F.L.O.R.I.A. from the book 'Mind Chi' by Richard Israel and Vanda North explains our memory enhancers.

We remember '**F**irsts' in life.
We remember '**L**asts' in life.
We remember '**O**utstanding' events.
We remember '**R**epeated' events.
We remember '**I**nteresting' situations.
We remember '**A**ssociation' through our senses.

We most probably remember our first car, and maybe even the number plate, our first job and probably our first kiss. In this instance, there's a good chance we remember our first yoga practice too. Likewise, I remember my first experience of someone taking something that didn't belong to them.

As a simple example; I could continue to resent that small act or I can choose to disentangle myself from that memory, use the forgiveness in my heart and let go of the feelings of anger that enraged me that day. Either way, only I am affected. It's helpful to understand that 'Wendy' has no idea of my emotions and probably can't remember that day either.

(She's probably in prison for bank robbery anyway!)

I've used a very simple example here from my past. However, if I were to continually be 'stolen' from, my emotions might grow stronger each time because I'm overloading on the same emotion and feelings, to the point where it affects the person I am, and the way others view me. Our brain is a very clever thing and it remembers even if we think we have a bad memory. We may have past experiences that repeatedly trigger an emotion in us, be it anger, sadness, fear, guilt, resentment, rejection and many more. In which case, this acronym is a good way of identifying where our emotions attach to a memory and its origin.

Identifying the source and understanding our emotions with our mature intellect, can allow the feelings behind our experiences to dissipate, as well as give us insight into why we felt such strong emotions around a recent situation.

We can take our negative memories and experiences that didn't serve us to our mats. We can practice forgiveness for ourselves and others. We can change a negative thought into a positive thought, through love and understanding. Wendy was young and did something that was socially unacceptable, but on a deeper level she believed by taking those earrings they would bring her a 'feeling' of something positive.

Asteya isn't just the act of physically stealing. It could also be identified as stealing the limelight, plagiarism and pinching other people's ideas. Stealing can be stealing from the earth or stealing our children's future. It can also be stealing someone else's energy.

If we all take a piece of coral or rock home from our nature trip, what are we leaving for our children?

Maybe we strive to be like someone we know, maybe there are people who have what we want. We want their wealth, their jobs, their lifestyle or even their partners. It could be as simple as wanting to be more like others in our yoga classes rather than honouring where we are right now, and let's face it, someone else might have put a lot more work into something than we have, so why do we have the right to steal from them?

'Try not to steel others energy'
'Be a radiator not a drain'
'Leave the room having lifted the mood, not lowered it'
'Be the sunshine not the storm'

When it comes to positive energy, we can aim to be as positive as we can, but I don't believe we can sustain it all of the time, because we're not perfect, our emotions and moods are not always the same and life isn't always easy. Nevertheless, I've had situations where I've come away from social engagements and felt physically drained having listened to hours of someone else's problems or angry 'offload'. We can drain each other's energy to the point where we'd like to lay in a dark floatation tank. Having identified it as a form of 'stealing', be it unconsciously, I aim not to take too much of other's energy and in return I aim not to allow others to take too much of mine. Is that selfish? No, it's self-care.

Someone can only steal our energy if we allow them to.

I became acquainted with a lady who, like me, was training to become a Life Coach. We met at our very first seminar. She had much higher aspirations than I, and wrote down that she wanted an income of £150,000 in her first year of business in contrast to the £15,000 I wrote in my book 'You need to put a few more zeros on that' she said, as she leant over my notebook.

As I learned more about being a personal coach my business plan became believable, I realised the time was coming I needed to stand up and tell others what I did, why I did it, and what they'd get from it. I was petrified of public speaking and melted at the thought of going to a local business event or worse, breakfast networking group, even though I'd previously been an aerobics teacher and was no wall flower when it came to voicing my thoughts. I bought a book on public speaking by Dale Carnegie; it suggested I read out a few lines to a family member, so I walked into the lounge where my two children were sat on the sofa watching television, and stood looking at them. They weren't aware of my thumping heart as I froze at the prospect of standing up and reading something out loud in a public speaking manner, even though I'd been reading to them for years! I've learnt that when we are afraid, we become self-conscious, we become aware of the chatter in our minds and the beliefs we hold about ourselves along with our shadow who watches and listens to us. Not only are we aiming to speak to others but we become aware that we're also trying to override our inner stories and ignore our shadow too. We are faced with someone who is watching us from an outside viewpoint and if we've ignored the plight of our shadow, the only 'person' that's able to speak is our persona, which isn't true, reliable or based on who we are - thus creating stress and discomfort.

Speaking from the inside, out
is therefor much more effective
than speaking from the outside, in.

It's nothing unusual to be frightened of public speaking, in fact, it has been widely documented that more people are said to be afraid to speak publicly than to die. (It wasn't either/or, just a question; 'What are you most afraid of?) So, in effect, most people would rather be in the coffin, than stand next to it addressing the mourners. I needed to face my fear and I knew exactly where my fear came from. At home as a child I wasn't given the freedom to talk whenever I wanted, maybe I spoke too much but my father would say a repetitive word, repeatedly until I was quiet. I'm not happy to share that word, but it made me fearful of my own voice bringing about feelings of embarrassment, self-consciousness, lack of confidence and even shame. What made things worse, was that my parents bought a fashionable faux leather, three-piece suite that squeaked if you moved your bare legs or arms on it. I often felt like I was neither allowed to speak or 'squeak' in fear of being told to be quiet. My father's bark was much louder than his bite, but this is a fine example of what makes its way into our minds and sticks around. The emotions attached to those events and subsequent memory affected me for years to come. I felt self-conscious and was in fear of feeling embarrassed or ashamed if I spoke up. Looking at the situation positively, it acquainted me with the floor which became a preferred, safe, and pleasant place to be.

As it happened my new coach friend was incredibly serious about her business. She invested thousands of pounds into a program with a 'Master Coach' in San Diego. As part of her investment she could invite other people to several events over the coming months and years. Sharon wasn't interested in the event that was on offer, named 'How to Be a Great Public Speaker', she asked me if I'd like to take advantage, since I'd said how petrified I was. 'Yes please' I said; so I *felt the fear and did it anyway.*

It was October 2010, I stood on the platform at Grantham station. I had to cross London, get on a plane to Los Angeles and get another tiny twelve-man plane to San Diego (to include massive ear protectors to block out the noise of the engines). I'd arranged to share a room with a woman I didn't previously know from Texas. We agreed that I would need to be as quiet as a mouse, as I wouldn't arrive until the early hours of the morning but would meet her when her alarm went off the following day. That mound in the bed, when I crept into the room, could have been anyone. I was too tired to care.

Every morning we had a complimentary yoga session which was exhilarating. One morning we were asked to dance around our mats 'Let go, feel free' said our beautiful instructor. We were chuckling and giggling.

'You crazy Americans!' I laughed.

The woman next to me replied 'You crazy British woman you!' It was such a lovely experience. Open, free and alive! Every morning should start with a yoga practice encouraging us to feel free in mind, body and spirit – but only if we want.

*Not enough time you say? A few sets of Sun Salutations
in our underwear, can set us up for the day.*

That first morning, we were asked to meet in the main hall, there were around seventy five of us in rows of fifteen. After the initial introductions a microphone was passed around from one person to the next, each of us was asked to stand and give a brief explanation of who we were, what we did, why we did it and what we offered. What? But this was my biggest fear! What was going on? I wanted to run away! I could see the lady next to me felt pretty much the same. I could literally see her heart thudding, under her skin; my heart joined in and started to thud too; you see, somewhere along the line, I'd made a huge mistake. Instead of the 'How to Be a Great Public Speaker' event I thought I was on, it turned out that I'd booked myself mistakenly, onto a course called 'How to Fill Your Events'. Talk about being in the wrong room, not to mention the wrong continent!

I didn't have a coaching business yet, I didn't have a website or impressive dot com like the others who introduced themselves before me; I didn't have an income from my business yet and I wasn't sure what I was going to specialise in either. I can't remember what came out of my mouth that morning, but I can remember that I was honest. I remember seeing others smiling at me, engaging and nodding, I was humble and open, I let others be where they were and I allowed myself to be where I was - I didn't try to be someone I wasn't and I didn't steal their details or facts. I told them this was my first step and it might not be as big as their first step, but it was mine all the same. There was no doubt that I was out of my comfort zone mixing with a few successful millionaires. I didn't tell them however that I'd booked myself onto the wrong course – too much information, instead I decided to just relax and go with it. There will be a reason I'm here I told myself, I trusted in that.

Yoga classes each morning brought us together as equals. Wherever we were, whoever we were, we all had bare feet. If that isn't humbling, what is? Yoga has no 'isms', no one is too rich, too poor, too tall, too small, too thin, too fat or too anything else.

The reason for going, getting it all wrong and staying on the course anyway, was to meet Toby Martini. He was a friendly and fun person and easy to talk to, I explained my fear of public speaking and admitted my faux pas. He laughed and said I needn't have come all that way and told me about a global organisation, Toastmasters. He said there'd be one near me at home in the UK, it turned out there was, one in Peterborough and one in Derby.

Never heard of Toastmasters? Anyone can go and have a wonderful evening listening to speeches from between two and twenty minutes. Toastmasters will teach you to become proficient in speaking in whatever circumstance you want or need to speak in. How do they do that you ask? Through experience and condensing speeches into limited time frames whilst highlighting key points and fundamental procedures. The aim is to become an effective, confident, creative and interesting speaker.

I arrived alone and sat at the back, as you do, but then I threw myself in the deep end, *feeling the fear* and raised my hand when asked if anyone would like to *have a go* at a section of the evening called 'Table Topics', an open invitation to speak on a particular subject for two minutes. 'I'll give it a bash' I thought! The only thing is, you don't know what that subject will be, until you're in front of people and at the front of the room. It was a pretty bad first attempt, but I asked myself 'What was the worst thing that could come from it?' They weren't going to throw me out if I made a mess of it, and I was there to learn. Gradually, over the coming weeks and months, I got better. I went from feeling petrified to gaining quite a few rosettes for Best Speaker. It wasn't easy and I often questioned why I put myself through it, but it worked. Would I get nervous if I had to speak today, this evening? Yes, I would. I don't believe our nerves go away; I believe we become more comfortable with our nerves when we come from an authentic place. As we become more proficient and relaxed in ourselves, the enjoyment outweighs the fear.

Just like anything including our Yoga practice. The more we do and the more we try, the more comfortable and competent we become. We don't improve as quickly just by reading about things or dreaming alone.

We need to move our feet and throw ourselves in.

Each week four members speak and after a break for drinks or dinner, four other members give feedback speeches on the initial four speeches. Other members are asked to be the evening's grammarian, a repetitive word counter, known as an 'um' and 'err' listener, and a timer. Roles are interchanged over the following weeks and months. There is also an opening speaker, a closing speaker and an evening's host. The evening is organised to convey a professional conference. Some people attend to listen to the speeches only.

Audience members are asked to write down a few words of feedback and encouragement for each speaker. It's an exciting time when you get home and read your way through your paper comments. My most valuable piece of feedback and advice was from an experienced member of the group called David, who recommended that I stand back once I'd invited another to the lectern or stage, to allow them to speak, giving them complete autonomy. I like that. Non-stealing, esteya; not taking the limelight from another person. I couldn't help but feel that it was just what my own father hadn't allowed me. At times, I wasn't given the autonomy to speak and be heard.

Letting others stand in their light allows them to be seen and heard in all their glory. That's what I learned from Toastmasters. I learnt that what we need to give others, was what I needed myself; acceptance. Having simply identified it, I became far less nervous.

Anjali Mudra is a salute, a respectful greeting. It's a well-known hand gesture, where we place our hands together at our sternum. It is usually accompanied with the word Namaste which can be translated into 'I see the light in you, I show you the light in me' and sometimes opens a yoga class and invariably closes one

When teaching, I aim to share what I've learnt with love and compassion and I hope that comes across. Instead of 'public speaking' and seeing myself as 'the speaker', the teacher or the centre of attention, I aim to turn it around. Instead, I'm sharing and giving what I hope to be an honest and open practice. We're not so much teaching as *guiding*. How can we teach and instruct, or advise on asanas to others when you are the specialist in your own body? When I guide, my aim is to encourage you to feel your own body, and your own way. To help you get out of your head and into your body, to bring thoughts into feelings and to let go of conditioned thinking. I allow myself to make mistakes and to share those mistakes. I don't edit my videos, instead I let everything happen as it would in real time. Minutes before my very first yoga class started, I had to take myself out of the hall to have a 'quick word' with myself. I reminded myself that feeling nervous is the same, or very similar to feelings of excitement. I naturally wanted it to go well, I was excited for sure and I was nervous too. I walked back into that hall and focused on everyone's *light*, knowing that everyone wanted my *acceptance* just the same as I wanted theirs.

If you want to publicly speak, but you feel too nervous, speak by showing others your light and concentrate on their light in return. We are less nervous when speaking from a place of shared acceptance

I became aware of why teaching aerobics felt natural whilst 'public speaking' didn't. I've recognised I'm most comfortable when I'm moving. I'm at my best when I feel physically free. When we're in alignment with who we are, our whole body communicates. Wearing gym wear, moving, playing music, throwing shapes, being with likeminded people, practising in a building that looks like a shed! It's all on my Bliss List and all adds up to an easier way of living and being.

I put my name on the list and spoke often at Toastmasters; public speaking started to feel much more comfortable and gave me the confidence to tell the local vicar that I wanted to give the eulogy at my mother's funeral. I spoke from my heart and shared things that were happy, things that were memorable and things that I knew would be on her Bliss List. I shared some of her firsts and some of her lasts. I shared what was interesting and outstanding and aimed to describe to everyone in that church that day, my mother's light. I did everything I could not to steal an ounce of what belonged to her in those moments before she was buried. At the same time, it broke my heart.

Sometimes we steal from ourselves because we simply don't believe in ourselves and our capabilities. We live a smaller life than we need to, using all sorts of self-abuse such as judgement, criticism and demands for perfection. We steal our own fire and energy.

4th

Brahmacharya
(Brah-mu-char-yuh)
Non-Excess

- To know what and when is enough
- Pleasure without excess

Brahmacharya is the fourth of five Yamas, being within the first limb of the Eight Limbed Path. In Sanskrit 'Brahman' means 'the divine' and 'charya' means 'the path', therefore if you are on the path of the divine, you are living alongside Brahmacharya. It is possibly the most ignored Yama due to the common misconception that it's linked to chastity and celibacy and so considered irrelevant. Subsequently, it was used to remind men to curb their sexual drive and energy, enabling the preservation of Prana to help them progress along their Yogic path. Historically, yoga was a practice for men only. It was men who brought yoga to the West in the late1800s and 1900s.

A traditional asana practice is completed six days a week taking Saturdays off as a rest day. Friday evenings were reserved for making babies.

My best friend at primary school told me about sex. Until then I had no idea. I remember it quite clearly, we were in the toilets where we would mostly take it in turns to push each other out of the way whilst singing a song entitled 'Take a picture of me' in order to monopolise the small mirror above the basins and admire our short fringes and freckles. On this day, I was in the left-hand side cubicle with the door open. 'I know how babies are made!' said Lynda. 'A boy has to put his willy in a special hole that we have', she said, pointing - 'down there'.

'Er' I replied, 'really?'

'Yes' she said, 'but first he has to suck your tits - otherwise it won't go in!' I didn't want to hear any more. It was disgusting.

When we live on the 'path of the divine', we live our lives in harmony with others, not thinking ourselves better and not using our own power, position or status for our own personal desires or gain. Brahmacharya is creating harmony in our lives, not overindulging, not eating too much or drinking too much, not becoming obsessed by people, careers, hobbies or exercise regimes. Those with a sexual addiction will not be using Brahmacharya. Not having 'too much' of anything brings us back into balance, working with this Yama leads us towards a higher place and vibration.

Raising our vibrational energy helps us feel lighter and creates feelings of joy, love and peace. When we go to our 'retreat' or mat, we can raise our vibration through acknowledging our body, emotions, actions and thoughts.

Ever been in a situation where you know you are seeking pleasure, but you also know that you are not doing the right thing? It could be something that gives us a little pleasure but instead, prevents us from finding and experiencing peace and happiness within ourselves? The ego wants to want, *more* than it wants to *have*.

Imagine something or someone you respect looking down at your actions. I privately think of this yama as the 'tut-tut yama' *an easy way of understanding and practicing Brahmacharya.*

For instance, for too many years I've had a thing for Kevin Costner. I'm not sure what it is I like about him, apart from his face, body, smile, stature, voice, lips, acting skills, eyes, legs, the way he walks, talks, eats and breathes, but there's something very special about him. Something inside my chest actually moves. I like the way he wears a pair of glasses. I love the way he wears a cardigan in 'Field of Dreams'. I adore him in 'Dances with Wolves' and he's irresistible in 'The Bodyguard' but what I'm trying to say is, could I restrain myself from running off with him? In the name of Brahmacharya -Yes of course! (Lie).

Brahmacharya asks us to respect our own happiness as part of the bigger picture of life, as well as thinking of the happiness of others. In terms of sexual activity Brahmacharya is practised within the context of non-harming, truthfulness and not taking what is not ours, also that we never engage in a sexual act with a partner from an egocentric perspective or as an object for our personal gratification.

When using Brahmacharya, we feel balanced and in harmony. Balancing postures can help us create self-awareness around this. How balanced do you feel?

Outside of a sexual context, Brahmacharya helps us look for imbalances or disproportion in life. For instance, I have a 'thing' for coats. Dean insisted on counting them and declaring that I have at least twenty-five in the house. (I feel the cold). Do I need this many? No. This is a good example of overindulgence, I am ashamed.

We might overindulge in food, exercise, sex, sleep, alcohol, hobbies, our pets, Netflix even! Overindulgence feels heavy to me. If I oversleep, I feel heavy, if I overeat, I feel heavy, if I watch too much television, I feel heavy. I know this in tangible terms too as yesterday the row of hooks fell out of the wall completely, simply because I have too many coats on them; a point well made.

When we indulge less, we feel lighter. I'm always interested and curious about the 'tiny house' movement in America. Those that choose to live in them appear to live simpler, lighter lives.

What if we overindulge in food? That last piece of pizza looks so tempting. My guru in India told me he eats to live and not to be full. The consequences of overeating may put a few extra pounds on - we all know that. Actions have consequences. If I had to live on one thing for the rest of my life I would happily live on porridge, I don't think I ever go a day without it. Hardly something associated with a problem, yet if that's all I lived on, I'd probably have scurvy by now. When we overindulge in any area of life, we tip the balance.

'The point in life is to know what enough is.'
- Gensie; Japanese Buddhist

Brahmacharya can also be a mental overindulgence in the name of obsession. Obsessions can manifest in many ways, but a common obsession is trying to be liked by others. Sometimes we push ourselves towards relationships or friendships that don't bring us happiness in the longer term. If we've ever been rejected by another it can bring on an obsession simply because the other person no longer shares our views around that relationship. The more they refuse to see our views or reasons, the greater our obsession can become. This can lead to behaviours such as stalking, comparing, desperation, pain and even depression. People who suffer from depression can get stuck in repetitive ongoing thoughts known as rumination, which is associated with obsessive compulsive disorder or OCD. It helps if we can break the cycle, cut loose, or walk the other way.

On a light-hearted note, I remember when I was around twelve years of age, I became obsessed with our paperboy who was a year older than me and went to the high school on the other side of the town. He delivered the Leicester Mercury. Oh boy, the lengths I went, to be noticed by him. I'd just happen to be out on my bike somewhere on his round. I'd push the paper back at him, after he pushed it through the letterbox. I even sellotaped the letterbox up once, so that he struggled to push the paper through at all! Then one day, I decided to throw a bucket of water on him from an upstairs window and that was the day I realised I had gone too far, and had indeed, an obsession! Poor boy – I did like him!

What about becoming obsessed with being thinner, fitter or stronger because we believe it will change the way we think about ourselves? A reminder here too, about the stress and strain we might be putting on our 'shadow' when we behave like this.

Obsessions can sit alongside our ego, which wants us to be exemplary. Stepping away from it plays a massive part in the practice of yoga. Unfortunately, with social media playing such a big part in modern lives we are constantly bombarded with a version of yoga that is not true to its form. Yoga is not about being a pretzel and showing the world how bendy we are, it's about listening to our body, mind and soul. Our energy is spent more effectively by listening to ourselves and not obsessing with trying to be like another or something bigger, which can create euphoric highs followed by emotional lows.

If we ask ourselves 'What do I need that doesn't involve stroking or protecting my ego?' It could be a walk, a rest, a sleep, time alone, some vitamins, fresh air, asanas? If we don't ask ourselves what we need, we're more likely to be led by the wants of others, their needs or our own knee jerk reactions. Creating a habit of making decisions based on what's best for us in the longer term, whilst respecting those around us is good use of Brahmacharya increasing our humility and compassion.

Creating a win/win described in the book 'Seven Habits of Highly Effective People', by Stephen Covey made a huge difference to my life and my relationships with others. It taught me that a win/win is the only way forward, it can help us reflect on all relationships, be it those we have with our partners, children, family friends or colleagues.

If you're happy and I'm happy, we have a **win/win**:
    We have mutual respect and harmony with one another.

If you're happy but I'm not happy, we have a **win/lose**:
    You may feel good, but I don't.

If you're not happy but I am, we have a **lose/win**:
    I feel good but you don't.

If we're both unhappy, we have a **lose/lose**:
    Something went wrong as we're both unhappy.

Brahmacharya reminds us to be mindful of the happiness of ourselves, balanced with the happiness of others.

Our Yoga practice helps us create and transmit positive feelings to the outer world. We're not aiming to be thinner, stronger, or anything else for another. Yoga is not an obsession but instead a way of being that nurtures our body and mind and brings feelings of fulfilment and nourishment.

In January 2019, I arrived in Goa for my Ashtanga yoga training. Dean left me at the airport with a nervous smile. I knew I would change, and I did. On my return my attitudes were different, I feel more relaxed and less obsessive or particular around what I own. Staying in a wooden shed for five weeks certainly brought my attention to the overindulgences I had and home comforts I took for granted.

Going away however, didn't sit well with one close friend, she didn't agree with me going, calling me selfish. People come and go throughout our lives, it's a fact of life. Some will stay, some will go, some will love us for what we stand for, and some won't. It's glorious and sad all at the same time. To be true to ourselves we must continue to grow, we must dig deep and stay on our own paths, rather than mould to the beliefs, values and opinions of others; we must enjoy those who accept us, and let go of those who don't. I believe we meet others for a reason, a season or the rest of our lives. With that, we trust to love but also let go when or if the time is right.

I'm very lucky that my husband is considerate and understanding, supporting my adventures. I am lucky to share my life with a partner who encourages me to continue to be who I am. I consider myself a free spirit with a need to fly, without that I would wither and become someone I am not. Dean tells me, it's my spirit that he fell in love with. He travels the world with his job, meets many people and enjoys it. I travel the world driven by my interests and passions. It's perspective.

Brahmacharya asks us to 'walk with God or Brahman' (or a higher being of our choice), to be kind, fair, respectful and balanced. To know what and when is enough. To step away from what the ego wants, instead enjoy our pleasures, purpose and passions without excess.

'Don't ask yourself what the world needs. Ask yourself what makes you come alive and then go and do it. Because what the world needs is people who have come alive'

- Howard Thurman; author, philosopher

5th

Aparigraha
(Apari-gra-ha)
Non-Attachment

- Non-possessiveness
- Letting go
- Choosing freedom over control
- Refraining from being 'owned'

The last of the five Yamas is Aparigraha, mainly meaning non-attachment, but also refers to non-grasping, non-greed and non-possessiveness of things or people. 'Moving through the world with an open hand and heart', Aparigraha asks us to accept and let go through life, it reminds us that we neither own nor possess anything. The word 'graha' means to take, to seize, or to grab, 'pari' means 'on all sides', and again the prefix 'a' translates to 'non'.

Maybe we grasp too tightly to others, situations or objects? Maybe we allow others or situations to control us?

If you've ever been on a rope swing across a river then you'll know how exhilarating it is. Imagine you're on the swing wanting to get to the other side; you're going to have to be 'all in' followed by letting go. If you don't let go, you'll end up swinging to a standstill, which means you'll get nowhere. To get to the other side, we need to trust and let go, even though we know for a short while we feel vulnerable or unsafe.

Holding on can do more damage than letting go.

I wanted to see if I could cope and detach myself from my family, friends, career, house, car, dog, clothes, jewellery, and what could be described as my *identity*. I wanted to be as 'naked' as I could without taking my clothes off. The question I asked myself was 'Had I become the things I surround myself with? Had I become the things that I've allowed to define me, my stuff, my way of living? Five weeks away, at the age of fifty-two, meant there were a few possessions and attachments to put to one side, I wanted to see if I even liked myself (how scary a thought is that?). I also wanted to experience how I would feel about sharing my life with complete strangers, many young enough to be my own children.

I arrived outside my little green shed, but I wasn't as happy as I thought because I'd asked to be in 'the garden area'. 'The garden area is full I'm afraid' said the petite Indian lady who booked me in. But I'd booked my shed already and I had an expectation. I'd dreamed of the yellow shed amongst the trees, the vision was clear in my mind. I needed to let go of my expectations in that moment remembering my mantra 'less stuff, no plans'. As I stood outside the very last green shed and the one nearest the beach under a very large and bright moon, all I could see was a symbol of love. Green, Anahata, the Heart Chakra. 'Is everything OK Manda?'

'Yes, thank you. This is perfect'.

According to the World Beach Guide, the biggest decision you've had to make at Patnem is whether to go for a cooling paddle or decide which shack to order a drink from. Patnem is one of the quietest beaches in Goa, and it offers relaxation and rest. A perfect place to take one of the many yoga or meditation classes on offer. The beach is wonderful, (be it there are a few wild dogs roaming around), the sea is warm, and the sunsets are breath-taking. Kranti, the school I attended, is the largest yoga school alongside the beach.

The rats were running along the top of my wall, in a small area of about twelve inches, just underneath the roof. Their tails were long and hung down the internal structure. I couldn't see their bodies clearly because it was dark, but I could see their tails and hear them as they scurried back and forth. The sea was loud with heavy crashing waves, perfectly timed, dumping onto the beach. I soon discovered I was nearer the sea than I'd appreciated, just twenty-two steps from my balustrade into the water which had little, or no tide. The rats were scurrying, and the street dogs were barking whilst the waves kept crashing. It was a sensory overload compared with my quiet village at home. I was tired from the long flight and the scary two-hour taxi trip with my twelve year old driver, (just kidding), followed by lots of admin and paperwork on arrival. My experience of India and the Indian way is that they love paperwork and stamping things! 'I just need you to sign this, and this, and this, oh and then this, and this, and then we'll be done; oh here's another, can you just sign here too please, oh, and this one too'. *Stamp, stamp, stamp.* 'Thank you, Manda'.

I couldn't sleep, so I visualised myself as Snow White in a favourite childhood film. The bit where she's in the forest surrounded by birds and woodland creatures. I told myself I was safe behind my mosquito net, even though I clearly wasn't and drifted off to sleep with the help of my earphones and my Spotify playlist entitled 'Me Like'.

Trees, birds, the sea, nature and sheds are all part of my Bliss List. We're not nearly as afraid when we feel connected to what interests us.

Kranti, our guru, said the next morning that I'd need to pay more if I was going to accept visitors. I was in India and you're never far away from a rat in India. He said, 'If you let nature do its own thing, nature will leave you in return'. Were they words of wisdom or was he just being cute? He was my guru after all; anyway, I accepted his beliefs and slept like a baby underneath my (imaginary rat proof) mosquito net. I didn't see the rats again, but they left me little brown 'gifts' daily. I lived to tell the tale and appeared to dodge Weil's disease.

The food was outstanding, but the bed sheets were tinged with shades of brown along with the pillowcases and towels, another opportunity to accept and let go, in this case, the idea of immaculate laundry. There were four cooks in the kitchen and three times a day we were presented with fresh, nutritious, and creative vegetarian food. Many yogis live their lives using the first Yama, 'Ahimsa' meaning non-violence and choose to be vegan or vegetarian. A huge vat of cashew nuts was put on the serving table most days. I sat and tried to work out what the cost would be in the UK. In contrast, there were just five washing machines and possibly, including staff, seventy or eighty of us using them, constantly. Two of the machines were responsible for turning their contents into a pale brown colour. I realised this after attempting a 'whitewash'. I smiled walking back to my little green shed as many others appeared to have used the same machines. Brown tinged clothes hanging over balcony's drying in the dense Indian heat. It began not to matter so much; I could literally feel myself letting go.

There is one main shopping street just off Patnem beach, it's filled with shops that sell silver jewellery, dresses, ornaments, mandalas, t-shirts, sandals and souvenirs to include a plethora of mala beads. Everything is priced less than it is at home, however much of the quality could be questioned along with the enthusiasm to do constant business.

Japamala or mala prayer beads are used in Hinduism, Jainism and Buddhism as well as Yoga for the spiritual practice known in Sanskrit as Japa. Mala beads are used to recite prayers, mantras and chants when meditating.
Mala threads have 108 beads

Renowned mathematicians of Vedic culture viewed 108 as a number of the wholeness of existence that means that the number 108 covers the whole galaxy, the sun, the moon and the earth. In Astrology the diameter of the sun is said to be 108 times that of the diameter of earth. Coincidentally, the average distance between the Earth and the Sun is 108 times the Sun's diameter and, closer to home, the average distance from the Earth to the Moon is 108 times the moon's diameter.

You have to walk before you can run, and likewise, you have to do one sun salutation before you can do 108.

Four times a year on the summer, winter, spring and autumn solstice, yogis are invited to perform 108 Sun Salutations as a form of 'physical marathon'. It's something we can perform alone or as a community. It's a physically hard experience but exhilarating too, where we not only create a massive feeling of satisfaction and achievement, but also raise awareness and possibly funds for a bigger cause than ourselves. Some use 108 Sun Salutations as an opportunity to mark an occasion or maybe create a new habit; starting something new or stopping something which means letting go of something that no longer serves us.

As a community, Yoga Sheddies have raised money by coming together on both the winter and summer solstice mornings. So far, we've raised money for Cystic Fibrosis, RNIB and Care International. Demonstrating a real appreciation for our health and our ability to enjoy time on our mats. Traditionally 108 Sun Salutations take place as the sun rises.

I was in heaven on the beach. I had a hammock on my porch, a sea view and a whole load of information to learn. Most days I swam in the sea, and every day I watched the sun go down. My alarm was set for five thirty each morning to shower before my practice which included standing in a large plastic bucket to soak my constant dirt-stained feet. It was dark and cold which I didn't expect from India, however by 10.30am it was as hot as I could tolerate. We practised yoga in one of the four outside Shalas as the sun rose. We had lectures throughout the day in the shade of the Shala roofs, often accompanied by monkeys running across them, and then another slower practice at night along with mediation, plus homework and a reading list to get through. Each night I flopped onto my bed before repeating it again the next day. It's amazing how quickly we learn when we do the same thing repeatedly, day in day out, up at five thirty, bed by ten.

The sunset amazed us every evening which felt warm, calming and nourishing. It was beautiful sitting in front of the backdrop of trees, the sand between our toes and the sound of the waves. A perfect environment to feel any emotions we had. If we missed others, we missed them more. If we felt sad, we felt miserable. If we felt joyous, we felt jubilant, smiling, hugging and laughing. When we're physically exhausted, our emotions are heightened somehow. Every day from six o'clock until six thirty the sun slowly went down. It was beyond amazing.

When nature stimulates our senses so deeply, we can't help but be affected. We once went on a boat trip in a place called Monterey Bay aiming to see whales. We were lucky, we did. We experienced a cow teaching her calf how to breach. They repeated the action over and over again, maybe six times, leaving us speechless and feeling somewhat connected to a bunch of people we'd never met before.

Sat watching the sun go down, my mind wandered to one specific joyous time in my life. It was in 1987 when I travelled to Australia to spend time with a man, I met in a university bar named The Deckchair, somewhere on the campus in Eastbourne. We were young; he was just twenty-two and I, twenty-one.

A million letters later and *feeling the fear and doing it anyway*, I ditched the idea of putting a deposit on a house and instead, arrived in Sydney having stopped in Singapore on the way, taking myself out for dinner and wandering around the city - alone. It was the first of two trips I made to Australia; on this occasion, we travelled north along the east coast stopping in motels and a small tent packed in the back of the car, then 'island hopping' before making our way inland, skimming the 'outback' and driving back to Sydney. It was an unforgettable trip. We were young, carefree and a bit wild. I smile as I remember one particular motel or shack, it was on a sheep farm in the middle of nowhere, where visitors dined in the kitchen with the hosts around a large beaten-up table. 'Steaks on t'night, howd'ya wan'it?' said a young woman gathering her laundry whilst peering around the room in order to move it somewhere else.

'Actually, I'm a vegetarian' I remember whispering, wishing I could hide under the table. I remember the sound of the kookaburras and cockatoos on that trip, the vast open space and feeling as free as a bird myself.

It was when he and I sat on the beach beside a town named Noosa that I realised I was incredibly happy and falling in love with this man and my life. I was also experiencing lots of firsts; hot springs, wild lizards, huge lakes, rainforests, reef fish and miles and miles of open space. We were healthy, happy and enjoying life. I had savings in the bank, a bag of clothes in the boot of the car and the company of someone I felt increasingly connected to. I felt a feeling of happiness that on reflection I spent a lot of time chasing for years to come. I was unaware that I was surrounded by many things that mean so much to my soul, many of which showed up later on my *Bliss List.*

It was this memory whilst sitting on the beach during this particular sunset that prompted me to tweak it. Whenever anyone asked me what my special place or fondest memory was, I always drifted to that beach on that day. Why? Because it connected to so much of what makes me feel happy. Meeting my husband and the birth of our children are the pinnacles of my life, but this memory seemed somehow set. I travelled to Australia twice, my then boyfriend travelled to England twice. He asked me to move to Sydney to see how things might work out between us. I was serious about our future to the point that I bought a wedding dress from a fancy shop in Hong Kong but I wanted him to come and fetch me – be my knight in shining armour. He didn't show up; so instead I met and dated other men but couldn't forget about him. We kept in touch and I called him some five years later, 'I've booked a flight' I said. 'I want to see you before I make plans to finally buy a house'. He told me he'd met someone, and that she'd moved in.

My ego tells me I'd have been better off buying a house in the first place and reaping the rewards of the late 1990's property boom? In fact, I could have been writing this from a holiday home balcony in Port de Pollenca right now. No regrets, I had the best time, even though that relationship broke my heart.

Ouch! (Big Ouch!) Totally worth it!

Our brains will remember a good memory because it will have attached itself to associations. We don't always want to forget a memory because it's a happy one, but instead, we can 'tweak it' for the good of ourselves, our future and our wellbeing.

I sat with the emotions of that memory for a while and let them come to the surface rather than push the image away as I typically would. I visualised the view and saw myself smiling as I walked onto the beach past the grasses and onto the hot white sand. I listened to my emotions and I located the feelings in my body, then I visualised my family, Dean and our two children on that same beach, along with Derek, our dog, wagging his tail with excitement. In my mind I could see them waving, inviting me to join them. I pictured myself smiling as I looked into their happy faces, I recognised the blankets and the picnic basket on the sand, and I noticed that Derek had been in the sea. I saw myself walking towards my family, wrapping my arms around them. Walking into what later became my future and my reality. I'd re-set that image.

This is simply how we can use the power of our minds, not to completely erase a cherished memory or feeling, but instead to upgrade or re-frame one.

Use your Bliss List, adding things you enjoy, people you have in your life now and items you cherish. I can't visualise that beach now, without my family waving to me to join them. Give it a go. It may take time but over time it'll work - I promise.

I received a text later that week from my ex:

```
'For your information, I've been diagnosed
with cancer. I thought I should let you know.
The doctor has said he can keep me going for
              some time.
              Ralph x'
```

My heart started thumping and I felt physically sick! I wanted to pack my bags and get on a plane that very minute. I wanted to care for him and do whatever it would take to help and support him. It was an overwhelming feeling, but of course, he had his wife and his own children and I have my husband and my own children and with all the strength I can muster, I couldn't and can't make his cancer go away. Knowing and accepting is hard.

A fact is a fact. If we aim to fight a fact we will always lose.
Going to our mats, creating good feelings and sending those
good vibrations to others is something we can do.
So, I did that.

On the last day, at the end of my yoga training, I stood and watched Sandra, my fellow yogini, be driven away in her taxi leaving a cloud of dust in her wake. Tears were streaming down my face for a woman I'd only known for five weeks. What was going on? We need to love to enjoy the full benefit of every experience, but to honour our future we must learn to let go too.

'How lucky I am to have something that makes saying
goodbye so hard.'
- Winnie the Pooh

We don't own anyone or anything and others don't own us either, we are not entitled to anything or any outcome. I learnt during that trip that we don't need to hold onto people and that letting go can in fact be quite exhilarating providing we continue to create new experiences. I've learnt that letting life drift through us and past us a little more, gives us space for new pleasures and what's yet to come. That's not to say that every relationship or friendship needs to end, but instead if we allow ourselves to let go of what was, we can enjoy the same relationships and what we offer each other, from this moment forwards.

I won't ever forget my last evening in India. I arrived alone and I wanted to spend the last evening and sunset alone. I watched the sun go down in a pair of flip flops and an inexpensive cotton dress from a nearby shop. My hair was a mess and I left what little makeup I took in my shed. I was as natural and naked as I could be and I felt happy, still and content. I sat gazing at the sea for nearly two hours and felt I'd achieved what I wanted.

I later created a painting of that sunset. I named it
'An Indian Sunset whilst eating a peanut butter sandwich'.

Here's a beautiful piece below written by Sir Anthony Hopkins. It sits nicely alongside Aparigraha and for any of us attempting (or who have attempted) to hold on, grasp, grab or refuse to let go of a relationship or friendship.

'Let go of people who aren't ready to love you yet!
This is the hardest thing you'll have to do in your life and it will also be the most important thing; stop giving your love to those who aren't ready to love you yet.

Stop hard conversations with people who don't want to change.
Stop showing up for people who are indifferent to your presence. Stop loving people who aren't ready to love you.

I know your instincts do everything to win the good mercy of everyone around you, but it's also the impulse that will steal your time, energy and mental, physical and spiritual health.

When you start manifesting yourself in your life, completely, with joy, interest and commitment, not everyone will be ready to find you in this place of pure sincerity.

That doesn't mean that you have to change who you are. That means you have to stop loving people who don't want to love you yet.

When you are excluded, subtly offended, forgotten or easily ignored by people you give time to, you don't do yourself any favour by allowing them your energy and your life.

The truth is that you're not for everyone …

And not everyone is for you …

That makes this world so special, when you find the few people you have friendship, love or a true relationship with …

You will know how valuable that is …

Because you have experienced what isn't …

But the more time you spend trying to make you loved by someone who can't…

The more time you waste depriving the same connection …

There are billions of people on this planet, and many of them will end up with you, on their level with their vibration, from where they stand …

But …

The smaller you stay, involved in the privacy of people who use you as a pillow, background option, a therapist and a strategy for their emotional healing …

More time you stay out of the community you wish for.

If you stop showing up you might be less wanted …

If you stop trying, the relationship might stop …

If you stop texting, your phone stays dark for days and weeks

Maybe if you stop loving someone, the love between you will dissolve…

That doesn't mean you ruined a relationship!

That means all this relationship had was the energy that only you and you hire to keep it in the air.

It's not love.

That's attachment.

That's wanting to give a chance to those who don't want it.

The most valuable and most important thing you have in your life is your energy.

It's not just your time because that's limited.

It's your energy!

What you give every day is what will become more and more in your life.

It's the ones you give time and energy that will define your existence.

When you realise this, you start to understand why you are so impatient when you spend your time with people that don't suit you, and in activities, places, situations that don't suit you.

You're starting to realise that the most important thing you can do for your life, for yourself and for everyone you know, protect your energy stronger than anything.

*Turn your life into a safe sanctuary where only 'compatible'
people with you are allowed.*

You are not responsible for saving people.

You are not responsible to convince them to be saved.

*It's not your job to exist for people and give them your life, little
by little, moment after moment!*

*Because if you feel bad or if you feel obliged' you are the root
of all of this by your insisting, afraid they promise you the
favours you won't give them …*

*It's your only fact to realise that you are the loved one of your
destiny and to accept the love you think you deserve.*

Decide you deserve a true friendship.

Wait then, just wait a minute,

And look how everything is starting to change'

- *Anthony Hopkins*

Being satisfied with where we are in our physical yoga practice
is a good use of Aparigraha. Being present and enjoying the
here and now with the strength and flexibility we already have.
Not worrying if we fall out of Warrior Three or that we can't yet
come into a Balanced Crow or Headstand. Let it go! Aparigraha
is about not looking at what we could achieve or could be
experiencing; instead enjoying what we feel now, irrelevant of
whether it works or not. Aparigraha reminds us to not grasp, to
let go, to let life wash through us a little, leaving us feeling better
about life, helping us feel lighter.

Who do we need to forgive?
What are we holding onto?
What do we need to let go of?
What do we need to see differently?
What needs to wash through us?
What do we need to lovingly and gently walk away from?

Imagine standing on a station platform with your heavy luggage. You have the opportunity to leave your luggage behind and step on the train.
Whenever you are ready - the train is always on time.

The Second Limb of Yoga
The Five Niyamas

1st

Saucha
Purity

- Purity in mind and body
- Cleanliness
- What we absorb
- Living without regrets

The Niyamas are the second limb in the Eight Limbed Path of Patanjali's Yoga. Saucha is the first Niyama meaning cleanliness and purity and can be practised on a number of different levels. Saucha is the first of the five Niyamas within the second limb in Patanjali's Eight Limbed Path of Yoga. The Niyamas are 'observances' and suggested ways of being. They are things *to do.*

A clean mind helps us concentrate on what's important to us, a clean-living space allows us to live healthily, and the quality of what we allow in our minds helps us feel joyous and happy. Saucha is the information we absorb, what we read, watch, touch, eat, smell and taste.

A physical dynamic flow, Vinyasa flow or Ashtanga class can lead us to building body heat and sweating, leaving us feeling clear minded and physically cleansed

I stood by my parents' grave as pleased as punch. It was two years after my mother had passed away and four years after my father. I was forty-seven and on the cusp of our daughter leaving home for university. 'Mum, Dad, someone has offered me a job!' It came to me as a surprise because I wasn't looking for anything more than I was already doing; I've been self-employed since I was nineteen. I'd recently supported a small business owner with a couple of coaching sessions. One of the managers contacted me, 'I hope you don't mind me saying but we'd really like you to come and work for us. We think you have a lot to offer'.

He went on to say 'I'm not sure where you fit, but you seem right for us'. It felt good. In fact, it felt exciting! Chris was offering me part time work which would fit nicely into what I was doing anyway, and with this, I'd be part of a team and hopefully be in a position where I could make a difference to something already on its way to being highly successful. Thing is; it was an expedition company taking people to places such as Everest, Africa and Indonesia. It made me lick my lips in anticipation of being involved. Unfortunately, they had heaps of admin that was a touch disorganised due to an influx of work, so asked if I could organise it. It was music to my ears as I love a challenge, only most of it was centred around Excel spreadsheets. I started working on them but after a couple of months, the light quickly started to go out in my soul. Even though I was only working variable hours, I'm not a 'hide in a room and work on spreadsheets' kind of girl. I hoped I might move into another position quicker.

One morning I enthusiastically suggested that if I were to make a reasonable difference to the business, I might go on one of the trips, they agreed, with that I went to Ghana the following October. We had a kit list which I knew all about because I was the one who sent it to the students, however I adhered to it too seriously, taking clothes I knew I would be happy mixing cement in, and only one dress for church. Sixty orphans were relying on us to hand make one thousand six hundred bricks within ten days. Many of the female students took beautiful matching t-shirts and shorts and playsuits and miniskirts, denim shorts and summer dresses; I looked more like 'Hard hat Jones' or 'Bob the Builder'. We all took our twenty first century iPhones to capture our experiences.

We were travelling to the Volta Region in Ghana, West Africa, where people had very little in the form of possessions. We were on a mission to help build an orphanage and had already been pre-informed that we'd learn a lot from the trip.

On arrival at the hostel, a one-story building set within a walled garden, I walked into what looked like a cupboard 'Ohhh grubby', I thought as I backed out, peering at the stained cement floor.

'That's your room' said the team leader.

'Oh, is it? OK thank you.'

The room consisted of a slim metal bunk bed which was hiding behind the door, and apart from a fan, that was it. I told my roommate I was happy to use the top bunk, because I enjoy a 'view' although I had to swerve my head to one side to avoid the guard-less fan, scalping me. The metal bed frame didn't include a ladder, so it cut into my feet and I quickly learnt it was better to climb up in trainers as flip flops were also too painful. The window had a rusty metal sheet with tiny holes in it which prompted me to think two things; it was there to keep something out and it must rain a lot. Outside was a noisy cockerel whose neck I would have wanted to wring a few times over, had it not been for my love for birds. Each night I added to the pre-existing sweat stains on the mattress as I flipped and turned under the mosquito net, at the same time, I grappled with my trainers at the bottom of the bed along with my 'anti mosquito long sleeved top' which was the last thing anyone wanted to wear in the dense moist heat, especially when the power clicked off, which was too often and the fan ceased working.

'If you buy a coloured water container you won't see the dirt or snotty bits floating in it' Chris said, 'You'll need to drink two litres of water per day'. We were there to experience a different world to our own. Drinking water from single use water bottles was going to add to the countries plastic problem and the lack of recycling available, so instead we were given water purification tablets to make our dirty water drinkable, bearable and safe. It made the water clean or 'pure', even though it didn't look like it.

It was like learning to swim again. Every mouthful was dirty yet tasted like a local swimming pool. If you wanted a wash, then the same water tank applied minus the tablets. The task was to find a black plastic bucket, (loitering somewhere within the grounds of the hostel) and fill it from the same tank. The lower the water level became, the browner and dirtier the water. You then either washed somewhere in the garden or you carried it to the bottom of the garden to the 'showers'. The showers consisted of six walls, making two shower areas with a hole in the stained concrete floor for the water to drain away. On top of the algae stained walls were several small buckets. You stripped off, took a small bucket and dipped it into the larger bucket, and washed away. Fabulous!

One morning ridiculously early, I took myself for a 'shower'. I was the only person there within the garden which was surrounded by large trees with huge leaves draping down towards the ground. I was standing with my head peeking up over the top of the wall, naked and thinking this was the wildest, craziest situation I'd ever been in. It was a magical moment; my mind was clear, my body was clean. The cockerel was squawking, and the vultures were staring.

Even now, in our tiny forty-year-old caravan, Dot, I'm proud that I can achieve cleanliness and even wash my hair with a jug and a couple of washing up bowls. Saucha is not only about being clean and unsoiled but also keeping a clean and tidy living space, clean and tidy mind, along with being aware of what we absorb, read, watch, touch, eat, smell and taste.

Each day, I walked past a dilapidated shed, I questioned if someone lived there or even owned it. Sometimes the door hung open. I could see there was little or no room for anyone to stand, let alone sleep.

Her name was Julia, it could have been Juliette or Julie, her name seemed to change depending on whoever I spoke to, and she accepted all three. Her family was made up of herself and her three children, two of which lived with her. They lived in a lean-to with the small dilapidated shed adjacent. It may have been a simple, or even an unacceptable home, but it commanded the same respect as any home, so after meeting her and speaking on several occasions I made sure I stood back before being invited 'in'. At night they slept elsewhere, somewhere within the village, I didn't ask.

The locals are advised to use mosquito nets, but I noticed they rarely do, choosing to make football goals from them instead. While her children attended school, Julia stayed at home and worked just the same as I do. The floor was solid earth which she swept until it looked smooth and shiny, she had no furniture other than one chair and one very low stool. I asked her if I could continue to visit her, she nodded excitedly, so I dropped by every day.

Julia insisted I sit on the chair, I insisted I sit on the stool, this affectionate argument happened at each visit for the rest of my trip. We were two women who looked different and lived differently, yet we were the same; our daily activities mirrored each other, both loving our children, both cooking, cleaning and working, doing our best for our families. She had an ongoing open fire and two large black pots, one for cooking food, one for washing clothes, along with a bucket of cold water which stood next to the fire. Her long dress blew in the burning breeze. When I pointed to the material of her dress flickering around her ankles and toward the fire, she smiled and dismissed my cause for concern. Along with her huge smile and athletic build she stood stirring the ingredients in a large pot made predominantly from corn, whilst I sat on her stool watching her. She laughed when I offered to help, failing in my attempt to stir the mixture, because I simply wasn't strong enough. Instead I later tried to help her wrap food in leaves which she then sold to the local shop; I was making a terrible mess even though I desperately wanted to help her. We laughed; she was so lovely. Unfortunately, we were under strict instructions not to eat anything that wasn't cooked at our hostel. 'Share and Die' was our friendly motto, so I politely but regrettably abstained from trying or taking any food from her. I regret that now. She was poor in monetary terms but wealthy in friendliness and spotlessly presented. We smiled, laughed and enjoyed each other's company for maybe an hour each day. We were sharing special moments and it was just that, so special.

The day before we left to return home, I asked Julia if there was anything, she particularly needed that I might be able to help her with; language was a barrier, but we seemed to make ourselves understood. I speak one language; she spoke many along with a few English words. She nodded and suggested a phone. Julia called it a 'battery'. I lay on my bunk bed that night; tears rolling down my cheeks, and into my ears, worrying and stressing over why she wanted a phone and not a supply of food or clothes or even walls for her home? She owned a dilapidated shed for her belongings. Her children came home from school at lunchtime to eat a mouthful of bread and take a sip of water, she did her washing in a pot over an open fire with water fetched from the river and to better their lives, they wanted a mobile phone? Who would she call? Maybe it was to call her eldest son; I hope so, otherwise I could only imagine it to be some sort of feel good gadget. A few brick buildings had satellite dishes on the outside walls that looked contrary to the surroundings as most of the dwellings were either sheds or traditional African huts.

I was asked by the head teacher during a visit to a local school, to teach a two-and-a-half-hour technology lesson to the sixteen to eighteen-year olds. 'Me? But I'm not a teacher, and I know nothing about technology! Can I teach the younger children instead?'

'No!' he said assertively, 'I want you to teach the sixteen to eighteen year olds'.

'Good morning all, my name's Manda, I've been asked to teach you this morning'. I took a deep breath and got on with it. It soon came to my attention that out of twenty five students, one pupil owned a computer and two said they owned a mobile phone. I was asked to teach a technology class with an old keyboard with a long cable attached, minus a plug, a computer mouse and a large textbook. I had to clear my mind of all my thoughts and bring myself into the moment, however it turned out to be one of the most enjoyable days of my life. Firstly, I invited each of the class to tell us what they'd like to do when they left school. Interestingly they all wanted to be either a nurse, join the army, or join the police. One boy surprised me when he said he wanted to be a journalist. He was one of the two who owned a phone. I hope he succeeded. After a brief chat I soon realised they were crazy about football, British football, so I suggested they formed five groups with the intention of designing a phone app, based on their favourite teams. To the headteachers dismay, I gave them the option to move away from their desks and maybe sit under the shade of the trees outside. A far cry from having to conform to what appeared to be a strict educational setting alongside the occasional use of a whip.

We are all the same. We all want the same or similar from life, yet what we experienced, and the way people lived was a far cry from how we live. This was the essence of our trip and our learning, yet I question if we created a big enough *win/win?* Maybe we were flaunting our affluent lives, inflicting others with our inexperienced craftsmanship for our own gratification and entertainment? Maybe we would make a bigger difference if we sent funds so they can employ local men and women to build their own orphanages? On the other hand, if we don't understand how others live, we might not be aware or connected enough to want to help. For sure, we were learning about each other's lives, be it we were showing these people what a westernised life looks like, with our fancy belongings. I was confused. Were we gaining more from them in the name of an exciting trip, than them from us? I felt uncomfortable for parading our ability to even travel outside of our own country and into theirs, as I was told that without thousands of pounds in the bank, they would not be able to leave their country at all. I saw what they don't have, and may never have, and I experienced them wanting more of what we have. We hugged their children for the duration of the trip and sat them on our laps from day one, yet we don't entice or send our children to sit on the laps of strangers here. Where is the middle ground? Lastly, is a mobile phone more important than walls on a home or do we teach them this unaware of the legacy we leave? 'I can't believe these people have so little yet they're still smiling', said someone standing next to me one evening.

'They're smiling because they're happy just as they are. We're the ones who stop smiling when we think we don't have enough', was my honest reply.

With that, I needed to find a quiet space to clear my mind and think things through. I was having a wonderful time, but there were lots of questions I hadn't expected.

On my return I had a long conversation with a university student, who had been on a similar trip and was writing his dissertation on these exact questions.

Saucha reminds us to keep our minds clear, clean and pure as well as our bodies and environment.

What effect do our phones or 'minicomputers' have on us? I embarrassingly spent an average four and half hours on my 'screen time' last week per day! Saucha reminds us to step away and do something else that may serve us better. Saucha also reminds us to spend time with those who lift our spirits and step away from those who don't. Saucha reminds us to prepare, cook, and eat, fresh and nutritious foods. To be aware of time spent using technology, television, phones or anything that takes us away from our true nature

Julia made me smile, we shared so much in a world that is so very different. We hugged each other for a long while before I left to get on the bus, tears pouring down our faces. I had made her a small parcel of things I bought in a nearby town to include some fancy plates and forks and any leftover cash for her 'battery'. I gave her the one dress I took and anything else she might benefit from. Lastly, I left her my bras which are valued as something only the privileged enjoy. Julia and her friend who she called her 'sister,' had made me a loaf of bread. She smiled the biggest of smiles. On the top she'd engraved the words 'I love you', Julia was crying, I was crying. I will never forget her.

On a practical level, your mat will need cleaning once in a while. Some mats will happily go into a washing machine; some companies advise that you hand wash only. Laying your mat in the bath and scrubbing it with a brush will do the trick. My cork mat becomes very dry; it works well if I spray it with water before I practice. Having a shower before our practice helps prepare our body and mind and naturally keeps our mats cleaner.

My travels to Egypt, India, Ghana and China and the people I've met, have very much helped me appreciate what I have. I've also learned from some of the poorest communities about friendship, love and acceptance. To appreciate our bodies, our ability to move, to digest food, even to defecate healthily which seems a bizarre thing to say until we can't. We have so much to appreciate on levels we rarely think about.

It was during that trip in Ghana that I became familiar with the Bristol Stool Scale. It enabled us to inform the leaders how our body was functioning without going into too much detail. The Bristol stool scale is a measurement between one and ten, one being too hard and ten, too soft. Why do I mention this? Because the Bristol Stool Scale is widely used in medical situations where people suffer from problems with their digestive system and bowels. Yoga asanas are believed to help keep the contents of our bowel moving in the right direction, ready for evacuation. In a traditional practice we always twist to the right before we twist to the left. If we consider our bowel, we twist to the right which lifts our waste up and across our bowel, then twist to the left where it travels down our colon ready for evacuation. Clever eh!

On my return from Ghana, I went back to working part time variable hours staring gloomily at the Excel sheets checking phone numbers, passport numbers and dates. I'm just not a numbers girl. It turned out they needed an administrator more than anything else and I needed to spend less time sitting and more time *moving*. Nothing about being an administrator was on my Bliss List. I thanked the company for their friendship, my time of employment and for taking me on a memorable adventure and handed them my notice. At the same time, I thought those Excel spreadsheets could go where the sun doesn't shine. I'm pleased I worked for that company, I learned a lot from them.

If anything in life isn't useful, beautiful or brings happiness we need to find the courage to change it, stop it, give it away, sell it or recycle it.

Saucha for the body
Drinking more water
Daily movement and exercise
Eating a healthy diet
Removing toxins through sweat

Saucha for the mind
Apologising when we're wrong
Giving ourselves time to mourn
Forgiving others
Being aware of distractions
Living in the moment
Positivity
Honesty
No or less regrets
Acceptance of what is

Saucha for your environment
A clean home
A clean working space
Clean clothes
Clean linen

Saucha asks us to de-clutter and live in a clean environment; to eat clean and have a clear and pure mind which includes not having regrets. Saucha asks us to step away from anything that prevents us from enjoying our lives and genuine nature. We begin to feel lighter, our minds become clearer and our environment begins to reflect it.

Not being comfortable in our own bodies can distract our asana practice if we constantly cloud our minds thinking we don't look the way we want to look.

Practicing yoga helps us become more aware, in turn we become more mindful over what we do, what we eat, drink, think and speak. Aiming to keep our minds pure through meditation helps us listen to our emotions and thoughts; by doing so, we're far less likely to react in ways that might not be right for us in the longer term. When we're confused, overwhelmed or in conflict with our thoughts, Saucha reminds us to find the time to step aside, cleanse our minds and allow ourselves time to create purity of thought.

Headstands are seen to be one of the hardest, yet most impressive, Ashtanga poses. If you're already doing headstands, you'll agree with me that we need to be strong but we also need to feel at ease. When we are, we literally tip into them. How do we get to this point? We work through the asanas, cleansing our bodies and minds from outside interruptions, stress and worry. We arrive at a place in the moment, happy and relaxed and pure in thought. It's then that this crazy bat shit pose works.

2nd
Santosha
Contentment

- Happiness
- Gratitude
- Not seeking

Santosha is the second Niyama within the second limb of Pattanjali's Eight Limbed Path. I felt I'd lost my way, when both children left for university, hospital appointments had become less frequent, thank goodness, but as a result I'd lost my purpose. I forgot to look inwards, instead I panicked thinking I would be offered a solution from an outside source. I had to remind myself not to look to far into the future, not worry about the past and not feel intimidated by others, which included my own husband and his successful career. I've always been happy and thankful for my hairdressing business, my clients and my ability to pursue other commitments and passions alongside. Santosha asks us to be happy with what is. The more we find appreciation in the present, and the more we trust what life has given us, the more our feelings of contentment will quietly and steadily find us.

Writing before a practice can be a great way to offload. I scribble away and get it all out. Sometimes I want a physical practice, sometimes a nurturing practice, sometimes I just cuddle a bolster and leave it at that.

When we 'boil down' what we want, we end up with two feelings, happiness and/or contentment. For many though, especially in the West, happiness lies only in the future, in the name of 'when I have this, I'll be happy', or 'when I've finished this, I'll be happy', or 'when I get to this standard of fitness', or 'this weight, or this shape, I'll be happy'; all connected to the ego. If we're not careful we can wait all our lives to achieve the happiness we've placed in our future instead of bringing happiness into the moment right now.

'The Dip' was created by Seth Godin. It's a great visual, and book, which highlights the middle section between where we are, and where we want to be. It explains many things such as, what is success, why only certain people achieve success and why some get stuck in the process or give up.

A Life Coach will help you get to where you want to be quicker and easier than if you try alone, by supporting you through 'The Dip'. This can be anything you want to Be, Do or Have. The interference that stops us, is nearly always internal thoughts, emotions, frustrations, and anxieties, rather than logistic or tangible barriers. Low confidence, low self-esteem, trying too hard, trying to be perfect, pleasing others, impatience and lack of knowledge all reside in 'The Dip', along with frustrations around goals that have been set by others which have little or no engagement for the person trying to achieve them. 'The Dip' is a place that can create emotional, physical, and mental stress leaving us feeling stuck and under too much pressure.

Life coaching sessions can reduce or even eliminate these interferences and help speed up the goal achieving process, however, my experience through yoga practice has taught me that little will help us more than repeatedly spending time on our mat. Why? Because time on our mat helps us clear the way. When we visit a coach we arrive with how we feel in that day. If we were to visit the same coach the next day we would arrive with how we feel *that* day - which may be different. We are ever changing with a kaleidoscope of feelings, emotions, actions and thoughts. This is the beauty of practicing yoga, we go to our mats repeatedly alongside how we are *today*, this day. Each time we revisit our mats we work unconsciously removing what is possibly or probably keeping us stuck in the Dip – without even knowing it. All we need to do is allow ourselves to be vulnerable, open, honest and transparent.

'We cannot consistently be who we are not'

Practising yoga is a way of life that becomes a healthy habit. It also brings us into this moment meaning we're not in the future and not in the past. Whilst we're in this moment, we can only be who we are right now, which is both humbling and gives us an honest foundation to work from. As we work on becoming physically and mentally stronger, our practice develops and increases our confidence, alongside feeling humble, relaxed, and accepting of life. We become aware of feeling happy in the moment as our body creates 'happy chemicals', such as dopamine and serotonin, both neurotransmitters used by the nervous system. As a result, our mood shifts towards a positive state. When we feel physically and mentally strong without the need for our ego, we're much more likely to succeed. The eastern practice of yoga asanas suggests and encourages regular practice. So, by practising yoga asanas regularly we continue to feel physically strong, we continue to feel mentally strong, we feel relaxed, happier and less afraid, and best of all, it all happens unconsciously.

Little will help us get where we want to be more successfully than rolling out our mat and being in the now.

I've grown myself and seen others change too, growing in confidence, through sheer determination but also though learning to put perfection down. Feelings around 'not being enough' is something I've struggled with, and others have shared they struggle too. We live in a society where bigger, stronger, and faster gets our attention along with prettier, thinner and younger. We get caught up in aesthetics, lifestyles, and incomes. Marketing companies thrive on our insecurities and drive us to spend our money and time on trying to keep up with others, suggesting we're not enough *without more.*

We'll benefit greatly if we remind ourselves that we have enough, and we are enough. Suppose we didn't have the ability to compare ourselves with others, we'd all be happier, wouldn't we?

I'm not strong enough
I'm not attractive enough
I'm not intelligent enough
I'm not thin enough
I'm not sexy enough
I'm not worthy enough

Irrational thoughts aren't good for us. They damage our self-esteem and force us to rely on our ego to survive this crazy world. If you've thought any of the above about yourself, you might want to bring a logical approach to the subject.

In what way might you think you're not enough?
Ask yourself:
- Where did this thought come from?
- Who led you to believe this about yourself?
- What assumptions have you made?
- Is what you're saying true?
- How do you know it's true?
- Can you categorically say it's true?

Our minds are smart and will believe what we tell it. If we tell it something often enough we unconsciously endorse it. Finding facts helps and breaks the cycle.

Example
"I'm not intelligent enough"
- Where did this thought come from?
  - *School.*
- Who led me to believe this about myself?
  - *Teachers at school.*
- What assumptions have I made?
  - *I assumed they must be right because they're professionals.*
- Is it true?
  - *No.*
- How do I know it's true?
  - *Because I run two businesses.*

Give yourself recognition right now that you are enough. We're all different for sure and we're all amazingly unique. We all have qualities that shine brightly; we're totally and undisputedly enough! Do yourself a favour and drop those 'not enough' irrational thoughts. You are enough!

*Ironically, the main reason people don't start a physical yoga practice, is because they feel they're not flexible enough. This is one of the reasons **to** practice yoga asanas.*

There are times in life when we wake up and for no reason, we have an internal dialogue telling us this kind of irrational nonsense. You may relate to those kinds of days.

If I'm feeling low and want to lift myself, I look at my bliss list as there is always something I can do, think about or something that lifts my mood. Not made your list yet? Here are a few ideas of how we can also raise our energy and vibration in the moment, bringing us to a more positive state:

- Move your body in any way, yoga asanas, dancing, skipping, running, anything that involves movement
- Take your shoes off and walk or stroke the grass or sand
- Bring your attention to your breath for two minutes or more
- Detach yourself from your outcomes, simply surrendering to the now
- Take a quick shower – cold if you dare
- Stare at a single object, a flower, a leaf, a stone
- Be creative, even if it's a quick doodle
- Sip and appreciate clean water
- Connect with an animal for a few minutes. Stare your dog out
- Watch the sun rise or set
- Gaze at trees

What about thinking we don't have enough in the name of tangible objects? We often don't realise we want something until we see someone else with it.

Same in a yoga room. 'I wish I was as good as that yogi over there.' If we never compare ourselves with others, we're more likely to be happy with the level we're at.

When It All Goes Wrong

I took his keys; I wasn't going to take any more of his crap! He was drunk and shouting obscenities at me in front of his friends. Next minute I was driving down the main street in his father's huge American style automatic car that I was neither familiar with, or insured for. 'Where's Bowmanville?' I shouted through the passenger window to the driver in the adjacent car, as we stopped at the traffic lights.

'Are you English?' The man shouted back, 'I have family in Derby!' It was before I got married, before children. Before going to India, before San Diego but after my trips to Australia.

One evening whilst I was out with a friend in Leicester, I met a professional basketball player. He was funny, intelligent, and tall! At the end of the winter season, whilst out walking, he wrapped his arms around me and said, 'I want to take you home', ahh, romantic words. I lived on my own, worked long hours and felt ready to share my life. I decided to prove a point to myself and others as some said I didn't have the nerve to leave this country and go to Australia, so I confirmed them all wrong and went to Canada to live with Scott.

I had no job to go to, no work permit and little money. I broke my tenant rules and sublet my flat to someone who later changed the locks and proceeded to dismantle a motorbike on my lounge carpet. Meanwhile, Scott's mother said, 'Don't you worry your pretty little self about money, assuring me repeatedly they would quite happily support me. Three weeks in, they changed their minds possibly realising how much I eat and asked me for a considerable contribution.

There are times when we feel frustrated or things are said that don't materialise, when life throws a curveball. I love the term 'issues in our tissues' coined by Tarah Brach, an American psychologist. Going to our mats or 'retreats', allows us to identify and release tension, stress, and frustrations helping us deal with situations whilst increasing our resilience.

I made the intention to walk from one end of the town to the other, and as always, with my hairdressing scissors in my bag. After three failed attempts of being asked 'Do you have a work permit?' followed shortly by 'Sorry, if not we can't employ you, can't take the risk'. I began to panic. My plan was to make up a number and just hand it to the next salon owner and hope for the best, but I didn't need to. Her name was Rose, she was very pleasant and seemed happy enough to break the law. I stood in the doorway next to the free-standing air-conditioning unit. She was cutting someone's hair whilst a couple of people sat at one side of the salon waiting for their appointments. 'Are you English?' She asked, 'Oh good, I like English hairdressers'. She then asked if I had my scissors with me. After quickly explaining that her stylist had called in sick, she asked if I could stay 'Any chance you can cut that man's hair?' She said, nodding towards the middle-aged man who by this time I'm sure, was concerned. I took my coat off, hung it up, washed my hands and invited him over to 'my chair'. I worked for Rose three days a week and loved every minute of it. They were possibly my happiest hairdressing days.

Money was coming in nicely as I also collared another illegal job at a Gold's Gym, running a crèche for over excited, crazy bat-sh*t, pre-school children; whilst their strange-hair-styled, parents built strong bodies pushing seriously heavy weights. It was at this time I became interested in the benefits of weight training which later led me to train and became a qualified YMCA, RSA aerobics instructor. Living with a professional athlete meant running, weight training and skipping was high on the daily agenda. I learnt a lot from him, but we started to fall out as he refused to find summer employment before his next basketball contract.

I found escapism in walking to a children's park nearby and sitting on the swings after purchasing large packets of cheese flavoured Doritos from the local mini supermarket. It made me smile, as at that time, there was a state tax and a federal tax; some foods were taxed, and some weren't. Crisps were taxed and it became clear, after a confusing conversation between two shopkeepers, that cheese was also taxed, so that meant there was double tax on cheese flavoured crisps but only one tax on ready salted. It made me laugh whilst feeling a little bamboozled. I'd sit on the same swing most days and in my own way, I felt happy, especially working with Rose, however over time I realised that I didn't want to spend my life with the 'Almighty Basketball Legend' as he jokingly named himself after a few drinks. My life with him didn't make me happy and staying in Canada wasn't an option, as it would only be a matter of time before I was thrown out; so I flew back home even though I knew I'd miss working with Rose and I'd miss the cute Canadian children. Building my business to its 'former glory' was tough. I also had to move back in with my parents again which felt like a big step backwards, especially since my younger brother had moved into my room. It was down to me to accept where I was and accept the situation I'd found myself in, whilst remaining grateful for that crazy experience.

Ouch! Totally worth it!

Going to our mat, whether it be to practice yoga asanas or to meditate, helps change the way we feel. It allows us to create space to be honest and vulnerable, allowing us to listen to our shadow. I learned from being a listener at Samaritans to go straight to the pain. By sitting with the part of our mind or body that hurts we're able to invite it to the forefront allowing it to dissipate. Identifying our pain helps us heal from it.

Climbing our Emotions

The emotional guidance scale by Abraham Hicks helps us identify where we are emotionally. Aiming to be one or two steps higher can help change our psychology. We're aiming to feel joy, knowledge, empowerment, freedom, love and appreciation but that may take a while and we won't stay there indefinitely because life isn't like that. However, if for instance we feel angry, we may finish our practice and find that we feel one, two or three levels higher up the scale towards doubtful.

If we feel bored, we may find afterwards that we feel hopeful. If we feel optimistic, we may finish our practice feeling enthusiastic. On the other hand, if we feel fear, depression, grief, despair or powerlessness we may not have the energy or inclination to do anything physical. In this case we benefit from meditation or asking ourselves who can support us. Be it a friend, family member, Samaritans, GP or another trusted party.

We must be kind to ourselves and if we still want to practice in some form, then to consider a yin, gentle nurture or guided meditation class.

Want to cry? Let it out.

The Emotional Guidance Scale by Abraham Hicks

1. Joy / Knowledge / Freedom / Love / Appreciation
2. Passion
3. Enthusiasm / Eagerness / Happiness
4. Positive / Expectation / Belief
5. Optimism
6. Hopefulness
7. Contentment
8. Boredom
9. Pessimism
10. Frustration / Irritation / Impatience
11. Overwhelm
12. Disappointment
13. Doubt
14. Worry
15. Blame
16. Discouragement
17. Anger
18. Revenge
19. Hatred / Rage
20. Jealousy
21. Insecurity / Guilt / Unworthiness
22. Fear / Grief / Depression / Despair / Powerlessness

Santosha encourages us to accept and appreciate what we have. I've caught myself thinking 'I wish I was as good as that yogi over there.' Why do we do that to ourselves? Just like life, if we never compare ourselves with others, we're more likely to be happy with the level we're at or situation we're in.

Life brings us feelings of delight, pain, loss, desire, greed and joy to name a few. We can become unnecessarily attached to our thoughts by either aiming to feel more of them or spending our time, pushing them away. If on the other hand we work deeper into our beings, we discover that we are not our thoughts and that we can re-set our beings to the ultimate value of happiness and enjoy this moment, right here right now. Happiness is said by many to be a choice.

3rd
Tapas
Self-Discipline

- Determined effort
- Fearlessness
- Tenacity
- Building strength and character

Tapas is the third Niyama, derived from the Sanskrit verb 'tap' which means 'to burn' or to evoke 'fiery discipline or passion'. Tapas gives us the fire and heat for positive change and refers to the discomfort that comes with breaking habits or behavioural patterns known as 'burning off the impurities'. Tapas asks us to push forwards even when things feel uncomfortable, when we worry what others think, or what we might think of ourselves. Tapas helps us to create our own motivation, to 'get started or 'get on with the job', which might be doing tasks, or poses, we're not keen on, making changes or changing direction altogether.

I like the expression 'Unlike trees, we can move'.

We can use the fire of Tapas in all sports, in work and our personal lives too, when striving towards satisfaction and achievement. We can use Tapas when and if we decide that life needs change and having the 'fire' to change it. The twists and turns of life certainly bring a mixed bag of results and outcomes and an array of emotions and feelings, there are times we do nothing apart from maybe sit on a swing and eat cheese flavoured crisps in which case, we're *oscillating*, resting or thinking. Then there are times to commit and move forwards, in which case, we're *advancing*. Tapas gives us the fire to make changes for the better. I'll be using the fire and heat of tapas to get this book in print for instance.

'Fate whispers to the warrior, you cannot withstand the storm and the warrior whispers back, I am the storm.'
- Jake Remington; Indie Author

The Indaba Yoga Studio in Marylebone, London, has some impressive classes on their timetable. I decided to book and participate in a workshop there. On arrival we looked through one of the studio windows and saw a few people laying on their backs with their legs and feet crossed behind their heads. 'Hmmm' I thought. I got changed and entered another studio where I sat down on my mat in anticipation. Dean left but sent me a message 'You're the bravest woman I know, see you in three hours'. It soon transpired that I was not only the oldest in the room but also the weakest and possibly the least flexible. I'd also unknowingly booked a workshop with one of the world's leading advanced dynamic yoga teachers named Dylan Werner, but I didn't realise until I got home and told my own teacher in Leicester. 'Didn't you know who he was, Manda?' he said,

'Ha-ha, er, nope!'

Set your life on fire. Seek those who fan your flames.
- Rumi

If I've ever used Tapas during my yoga practice, it was on that day. The course was titled, 'Inverting the Backbend', which means backbend poses whilst in a handstand. I was definitely the least capable in the room, but I gathered all the 'fire' and strength I had and did my best. I felt amazing at the end!

Within yoga asanas, tapas can be practising postures we don't like or holding a posture for that bit longer, having the self-discipline and will in life and finding our warrior within. Tapas is the fervour for being the best we can be.

'Did you bring the sleeping bags?' I asked.

'No!' Dean replied. He often jokes, so I thought nothing of it. We arrived at our 'Fisherman's Blue' painted beach hut, 50 South Promenade, Sutton-On-Sea and as always, I instantly cleaned the windows to make them sparkle and complement our sea view.

At some point each year we'd spend a night away on our own, sleeping in our seaside shed after going out for dinner at a nearby Italian restaurant. It was cold, dark and windy walking down the seafront, which according to council rules, we weren't permitted to sleep in.

'Where are the sleeping bags?' I asked.

'I told you, I forgot them,' Dean said.

'I thought you were joking!'

Think of a shed, now think of a blue shed, and now think of a blue shed next to the sea. No electricity, no heating, no water, blowing a gale and now, no sleeping bags either.

We put on coats, hats, scarves and even gloves and attempted to sleep on the two-nylon camp-beds pushed together with (wait for it), the chequered blue plastic tablecloth acting as our duvet. As the night progressed, it got colder and colder, unaware too, of the unusually high tide. Periodically, we lit the gas cooker but thought better of it as it's rather a dangerous thing to inhale alongside the fact that it creates a damp atmosphere and made our plastic 'duvet' feel cold and wet. I sat up abruptly at 3am 'I can't sleep, I'm literally freezing!' I shouted out!

Dean too sat up; aiming to solve the problem, 'Would you like the windbreak?' he asked. We laughed and laughed as we considered the prospect of not only spending our wedding anniversary under a plastic tablecloth but also a stripy synthetic windbreak with wooden poles!

> *Teeth shine like stars*
> *Ears curl like cabbage leaves*
> *Eyes sparkle like wet pebbles on a beach,*
> *Smiles, smell of ale,*
> *The man in the moon is wide awake,*
> *Whilst we're drunk on laughter.*
>
> *- Manda*

We don't have to have the best; we don't have to be the best. We don't have to enter a competition of life; we don't have to win, and we don't have to impress. We can build our own fire with whatever we want.

> *Tapas. Whatever you want to start, stop, do more or less of, make it work, make it happen.*
> *We're stronger than we think we are.*

During Asanas, use Tapas along with your bandhas (energy locks) to hold that posture a bit longer. Try thinking about your feet touching the mat, bringing your attention to your breath, or figuring out which way you should be looking with your gaze.

If you want to practice once a week, commit to your decision. If you want to practice twice a week, use your determination. If you want to practice six days a week, use self-discipline knowing you're building strength and character. The fire of Tapas brings us self-discipline to get started and keep going.

> *'Build your own fire'. 'Paddle your own boat'.*

4th
Svadhyaya
Self-Study

- Taking responsibility for ourselves
- Not blaming others
- Self-reflexion
- Journaling
- Looking into our own mirror
- Noticing our own emotions

As I'm learning, re-learning, remembering, and affirming what I already know, writing this book is the best example I can give for Svadhyaya, the fourth Niyama.

'The person practising svadhyaya reads his own book of life,
at the same time that he writes and revises it'
- B.K.S Iyengar; founder of Iyengar Yoga

During my coach training we did a lot of self-study, a lot of 'inner work', reflection and questioning. I learned a lot about human psychology, what makes us who we are, what we want, why we have such strong opinions, why we scrutinise details or get angry or argue. We are all unique, like a kaleidoscope; turn that wheel just a tiny bit, and everything changes. If someone wants to be supported in a coaching environment, they might share their story one day, and yet the next it could be different because their kaleidoscope moved. Just like the weather, our situation, thoughts, emotions, and actions are constantly changing.

The only thing we can be one hundred percent
sure of, is change.

'Why are you crying?' Mum asked. I didn't want to share my thoughts that my beautiful mother probably wasn't going to leave the palliative care hospital. She looked bright and peaky, even though she was extremely unwell. 'Oh, I am sorry', said the lady who overlooked serving my mother's lunch 'I thought your Mum was a visitor, she looks so well'. Opposite there was a young woman sitting upright in bed and sitting by her side on a chair was another lady who looked slightly older. We noticed one another and shared unfortunate smiles as we came and went. She sang softly and beautifully, in what sounded like one of the many Indian languages. It later became apparent that the lady laying in the bed next to her was her younger sister.

Life seemed to shrink into a very small and intense environment. There were four beds in the bay alongside four patients and family members who were experiencing change at a rapid rate. Within twelve days my lovely Mum went from looking healthy to being very poorly. Her doctor advised us that 'Mum could pass away at any moment'. The hospice Chaplain suggested we leave our mother regularly and 'go and have a coffee', as many, he said, 'prefer to pass away alone'. As a family, we were hanging on to every belief and piece of advice we could. We endured countless coffees in the dining area adjacent to the bay to return to our wonderful warrior who refused to let go. The lady opposite continued to sing and hum and we both continued to acknowledge each other understanding our shared anguish and distress. All four patients were spending their last days on that ward. An older lady in the bed diagonal to my mothers, passed away first. Then the lady to her right that evening. It felt like a death factory. I went for more and more 'coffee breaks' believing that the advice must be correct and that by doing so, I would give my mum the relief, and way out, she so unwillingly faced.

The young woman opposite passed away in the early hours the following morning which increased my anguish further. Soon after, her relatives arrived. A large Indian family congregated in the dining area. There was little left for them to do apart from accept, mourn, make plans for a funeral, and mourn some more. I was having yet another 'coffee break', and about to make my way back, but first I wanted to gain the attention of the lady who sang. As I stood up to view the room, she too, saw me. We both walked meeting in the middle, we said nothing but instead hugged each other in a physical act that we both one hundred percent understood. Not a word had been exchanged between us in nearly two weeks and not a word was spoken in that moment. It was pure compassion and respect between two people on a basic human level. A moment that will stay with me forever. My mother passed away three days later. I, along with my sister and sister-in-law, were with her, and I'm so very grateful to have been present.

I continue to remind myself that we cannot fight a fact. If we do, we will always lose. We must accept and allow life, its many situations, illness, and death to take its course. My mother called me her sunshine; she was my sun. At times, we would laugh until we cried, we could talk for hours and hours and never get bored. My mother, born Franziska Maria Beckers, was an incredibly loving, kind, and generous woman who taught me so much about love and life.

Paul Grilley, a globally recognised teacher for Yin yoga shared a story that I will attempt to share with you in my own words:

A young woman's only son died. She was so distraught that she went to Buddha to ask for his help. She explained that her young son had passed away and that she wanted and needed him back. Buddha said he could help her and instructed her to come back in two weeks with a bowl full of rice, the only stipulation being that she could only bring rice from households that hadn't experienced death or loss.
She arrived back to Buddha with an empty bowl. He explained that she must learn and accept that all families suffer loss through death and that even if he could save or bring back her son, he couldn't guarantee that he, or she, wouldn't suffer pain or die at a later time.

Svadhyaya reminds us to notice our own experiences and reflect on them. Losing my parents was incredibly painful, losing my Mum was heart-breaking, it felt like I was the only person ever to have lost their mother, but of course, pain and loss is in every family and regrettably, part of life. As I've reflected over the years, I've become more thankful and grateful for the life she gave me, for our years together and to have spent valuable and precious time with her. We often wait until the end of life to ask for more time, instead we must value and spend more time with those we love now, while we can.

Yoga cultivates self-knowledge in the name of Svadhyaya. Being on our mats increases our understanding of ourselves and the life we live.

Holly was looking deep into my eyes, and I was looking deep into hers. She had pleasing, large brown eyes. We were both sitting cross legged after being asked to find a partner and sit down. 'Please look deeply into your partner's eyes for ten minutes and refrain from looking away'.

'Ten minutes - that's a long time!' It wasn't just us, all twenty-two of us on the course were invited to take part. The task gave us varying levels of psychological discomfort, I held my gaze into Holly's eyes and hers into mine. I became self-aware and self-conscious of my blinking, swallowing, and breathing. The urge to look away was immense. The 'onion layers' strip away quickly showing our *deeper levels* in full glory, there is nowhere to hide. Someone is looking straight into your soul and you in turn are looking straight into theirs. If one of you looked away, the other was instructed to redirect their attention back to your eyes. Trying hard to push my shadow away was challenging but after only a few seconds my shadow made its appearance again. It's like you're hanging your dirty washing out for all to see. Your shadow becomes 'real' and suddenly it has the autonomy to be seen, and silently heard. Holly, through my eyes, could see me, and my thoughts; at the same time, Holly is experiencing the exact scenario. She too is feeling vulnerable and transparent. Our shadows are raw, real, and honest and you might cry, possibly sob when your shadow steps forward.

We forget that others feel the same or similar pain as ourselves. We forget that others have similar experiences, and we forget that others also have a shadow that they are aiming to push away and keep secret. As our deepest fears drive through us, we realise that others are fundamentally the same. When we look deep into another's eyes, we discover that we see ourselves. Through this knowledge we open a door inviting us to become wiser, kinder, more curious, more vulnerable, and less afraid.

> *'Maybe you are searching in branches for what only appears in the roots.'*
> *-   Rumi*

We can practice Svadhyaya through meditation, journaling, reading, writing, and spending time in nature. During our yoga practice we can work deep into our bodies, and feel where we may be holding tension or pain from present or past situations. Sometimes we find tension trapped in our little fingers or wrist, or on one side of our neck, or deep within our shoulders, abdomen, or hips. Giving ourselves time to acknowledge where we're holding tension helps us learn to release and let go.

Studying ourselves may include writing a journal, writing a book, or listening and learning from within during meditation. Tears, joy, gratitude, sadness, or anger, whatever it may be, let it all come to the surface. Laugh, cry, dance, and shout. Whatever it takes, do it like no-one is watching.

5th

Isvara-pranidhana

(Ish-va-ra-pra-nid-hah-na)
Surrender

- Letting go
- Living between effort and surrender
- Dedicating our practice to another

Isvara-pranidhana is the last of the Niyamas and invites us to observe life beyond ourselves making each action an offering to something bigger. Once we've observed ourselves and our lives, Isvara-pranidhana also invites us to let go.

I was dedicating my yoga asanas and practices to those I love. I now realise through the essence of Isvara-pranidhana, that I serve more by looking wider. I often dedicate my practice to *every person* on our planet who is blind, has an eye condition or struggles to see. *Every person* who has Cancer or Parkinson's and to *all those* who endure the painfully frustrating weeks before and during their treatments. Whether we are spiritual or not, Isvara-pranidhana invites us to support the whole world to be a better, more loving, and compassionate place.

If we really want to benefit from our yoga practice, we need to allow it to seep from our mats and into our lives. Not only does our body become exercised, stretched, and strengthened but so do our minds and hearts.

Yoga translated, means to unite our minds, body, and spirit. To unite and connect us with others and to unite as a universe. Yoga can also mean disentanglement, providing an invitation to address and let go of our fears, worries, concerns and pain. Yoga in no way forces the idea of God or religion upon anyone, instead, we're invited to surrender and have faith in something bigger. Bigger than just ourselves – whatever that is to us.

What about God? Emma Newlyn, a yoga teacher from The Yoga Space, helps to describe this: 'Here (within this Niyama) there isn't a Godlike figure we are supposed to worship or devote our actions to at all, rather 'God' represents this collective consciousness, and therefore represents all of us too'.

A good few years ago, a friend lent me a book on 'Guardian Angels'. I was intrigued. It took me on a journey and asked during each chapter that I visit my newly created metaphorical 'temple'. This could be anything I wanted it to be from an umbrella sat by a river to a magnificent castle. During one chapter, it caught me by surprise when the author asked what my Guardian Angel's name is. My reply was ... Clifford. Clifford? Where the hell had that come from?

Clifford has become a powerful figure in my life. Whenever I see a white feather, I assume Clifford is around and looking over me. I hear myself thinking, 'Everything's going to be fine'. Now this can be nonsense, or it can be quite useful. That is up to us, but a good use of Isvara-pranidhana all the same.

Who or what do you want to give your worries to?
It's completely up to you and personal

– and unlike me, you don't have to tell a soul.

Many of us want to control life, we have tantrums if things don't go the way we want, ignorantly refusing to notice there may be another way opening for us that may suit us better. If we step back and imagine something bigger than ourselves having more or ultimate control, we create a space. Creating a space allows us to let go and relax, it could be likened to a big exhale. We can surrender in many ways, surrender to the truth, surrender to what we're trying to fight. It could be as simple as surrendering to sleep instead of staying awake.

Surrendering our ego and our selfish desires is very closely linked to the concept of 'letting go' and 'non-attachment', which is a focal point of the Bhagavad Gita.

The Bhagavad Gita is the sixth book of the Mahabharata, one of India's most famous epic poems. It is suggested to have been completed around 200 CE. Many see it as the first yogic scripture. Gita, like all great works of literature, can be read on many levels: metaphysical, moral, spiritual, and practical.

Life is a balance between what we can control and what we can't. Learning to live between effort and surrender is a good use of Isvarapranidhana. There are elements of my life where I continue to try, and other areas where I've chosen to surrender, deciding to trust that what will be, will be. Believing in our own lives with our whole hearts, whilst trusting in something bigger than ourselves, presents us with more support than we might imagine.

You might want to:

Dedicate your practice to another or others.

Create an offering. Light a candle. Allow yourself to be in the mood for spiritual surrender.

Be open to signs; white feathers, birds, words, sounds.

Assume the best in everything. Assume good outcomes.

Give your worries to something you believe is bigger than yourself. In my case, my Guardian Angel, Clifford!

I was the type of person,
That held onto things too tight,
Unable to release my grip,
When it no longer felt right,
And although it gave me blisters,
And my fingers would all ache,
I always thought that holding on,
Was worth the pain it takes,
I used to think in losing things,
I'd lose part of me too,
That slowly I'd become someone,
My heart no longer knew,
Then one day something happened,
I dropped what I had once held dear,
But my soul became much lighter,
Instead of filled with fear,
And it taught me that some things,
Aren't meant to last for long,
They arrive to teach you lessons.
And then continue on,
You don't have to cling to people,
Who no longer make you smile,
Or do something you've come to hate,
If it isn't worth your while,
That sometimes the thing you're fighting for,
Isn't worth the cost,
And not everything you ever lose,
Is bound to be a loss.

- E.h.

Surrendering thoughts,
Soothing moon.

Scattering seeds,
Oceans, deep.

Shining light,
Worries leap,

Eyes closed,
Deep sleep.

\- Manda

The Third Limb of Yoga

Asana
(Ass-a-nah)
The physical practice of yoga

Asanas are the third limb of the eight limbs of Patanjali's Yoga. Asanas are physical postures; I've got into the habit of saying 'ars-an-ah' like Mrs. Bouquet/Bucket. I suppose it's a bit like the familiar morning coffee, some say 'lar-tay' and some say 'latt-ay'. I believe the correct pronunciation is 'ass-a-nah' as you may have noticed that every Sanskrit name for each posture ends in 'asana', Padangust*asana*, Prasarita Padottan*asana*, Virabhadr*asana* and so forth. The word 'asana' translates to 'sit down', which suggests that most postures were originally practised on the floor.

If you are anything like me, the physical act of yoga is what brought you to the practice. Maybe you wanted to tone up, strengthen your body, increase your flexibility, or improve your balance. Sri Pattabhi Jois wanted that for us too by suggesting we start with the third limb. It's good to know that we're in the right place and if you're a newbie to yoga, then you too are 'in exactly the right place' by starting with your poses. As our practice unfolds, we find that we can sit for longer, listen to our minds and connect to ourselves and our minds on a deeper level.

Many people enjoy the physicality of yoga and choose the physical aspects only. Some choose to practice similar movement patterns in the name of Pilates choosing this form of modern kinesiology rather than being attached in any way to the philosophy or spiritual aspects of yoga.

The modern founder of Ashtanga yoga Sri Patabi Jois (pronounced 'Joyce'), was born on 26th July 1915. The word 'Sri' is a prefix meaning honour. He was the son of a Brahmin priest and astrologer who allegedly at the age of twelve ran away with two rupees in his pocket to study with his guru Tirumalai Krishnamacharya after seeing him at a demonstration. For one or two years he begged for food and slept in a dormitory room with a friend. Three years passed before he wrote to tell his father where he was. He got a place in college and remained there from 1930-1956 eventually earning a professorship in Advaita Vedanta. He taught there until 1973.

Advaita Vedānta is a school of Hindu philosophy and is a classic system of spiritual realisation in Indian tradition.

Being spiritual describes having a sense of peace and purpose whilst feeling connected to everything. Those who consider themselves spiritual, search for meaning in life.

A Traditional Yoga Class

In 1948, Sri Pattabhi Jois opened his own school in Mysore, India, named The Yoga Research Institute. Often referred to by his students as 'Guruji', meaning guru. Guruji introduced the popular Ashtanga style of yoga to many in the Western world, including The Beatles and Madonna. It was he who created a system called The Ashtanga Series, of which there are six. A Primary, Intermediate and four Advanced series all with a set number of postures to include the same fundamental opening and closing poses.

When I walk Derek, our dog, I often go the same way around the fields and tracks or the same way around the parks. I know how long it takes, what I'll get from it and what I'm likely to see. I do love adventure, but I also like familiarity and repetition. If you're someone who enjoys repetition like me, then a traditional Series One, Ashtanga class, could be perfect. The same poses in the same order, taking approximately the same time to complete, being around ninety minutes. A traditional practice quickly becomes familiar, and attention can be directed inwards towards the breath. In this way it becomes a powerful meditation in movement.

The aim is to get the breath and body moving and flowing together. The first time we experience this happening, can be an emotional experience indeed, and signifies we are working deeper within our *Koshas*. Teachers in the West mostly teach *Series One* and some of *Series Two*, either as a traditional practice or creatively blended as a Vinyasa flow. I can count on one hand how many people I know who can complete all of *Series One*, accomplishing all poses with no modifications. Modifying poses is perfectly acceptable and makes *Series One* achievable and enjoyable for most.

Sri Pattabhi Jois wrote just one book, entitled The Yoga Mala, starting in 1958 until it was first published in 1962, translated into English in 1999. I found it an intense read at first, however, over time I've found myself re-visiting it regularly. The Yoga Mala is *the* book to learn the sequential form of Ashtanga Yoga. Each posture has a unique amount of breath counts, a certain place to stare (or rest one's eyes), a certain foot and hand position and the use of certain Bandhas or energy locks.

The name 'Mysore' is not only a place in India but is also used to describe a class where practice includes a chosen series completed alongside other yogis, in silence; practised at your own pace using full or modified poses.

The Primary Series or Series One is known as Yoga Chikitsa meaning yoga therapy with an aim to *purify and cleanse the body* and *heal the disturbances of the mind*. Practitioners complete forty-one postures over an approximate ninety-minute period. Traditional Ashtanga classes also start and end with a chant in Sanskrit, which give thanks to Patanjali and yoga teachers who have passed on the yoga traditions. The closing chant, wishes the whole world to be happy and peaceful. Both chants separate our practice from day-to-day life. Many teachers prefer to invite practitioners, to spend a short while at the beginning and end of a class, concentrating on their breathing and a short meditation.

Ever heard 'Om shanti, shanti, shanti?'
It's a mantra, greeting and parting salutation used in meditations, yoga practice and Indian religions.
Often chanted at the end of the opening and closing chants.
The word shanti means a deep and profound level of peace.
According to Yogapedia, when chanted three times 'Om shanti, shanti, shanti', means 'Om peace, peace, peace' representing peace in body, mind, and spirit.

During my training, we practised a Mysore (own pace) class every other day. It wasn't something we were particularly excited about to start with, as we preferred the guidance of a teacher, but over time we all agreed, it became our favourite. It allows us all to measure our ability, strength, flexibility, and memory whilst creating a stronger sense of self. Practising together also creates a spiritual energy. The concept within each series was initially to master each pose before moving onto the next. It can take practitioners months or even years.

'It's not about putting one hand further forward or wanting to move onto the next pose quickly', he says 'It's about being able to concentrate.'

- Prasad Bhatdundi

Spinal Motion

Moving our spines in all six directions of flexion, extension, lateral extension to the left and right, and twisting to the left and right, keeps our spines mobile, supple, and lubricated. Our spines play a vital role in housing and protecting our central nervous system and is both the physical and psychological centre of our being. If our spine could speak, it would ask us to create movement. According to HR Review, back pain causes an estimated three million people to take time off work in Britain per year.

It was here that an Ashtanga style of yoga was perfect for me and my chronically painful back. I had very little core stability, so a style of yoga that creates strength and mobility whilst protecting joints was good for me. My legs shook and felt unstable, I also felt as though I wobbled as I walked. I was diagnosed with Ankylosing Spondylitis, Sacroiliitis and was also told I was hypermobile, which is sort of a contradiction to the disease. If yoga hadn't improved how I moved and how I felt I wouldn't be writing this now.

Yoga is like a geologist for the soul, it can show you where to dig, and what to dig for, but the digging you must do yourself.

The Four Principles of Ashtanga Yoga

There are four main principles of Ashtanga Yoga. Breathing, Bandhas, Drishti and Vinyasa. When we first start to practice yoga asanas, we find we're concentrating so much on the actual postures that we pay less attention to all four principles; totally understandable, however, over time we get used to moving our bodies which allows us to include the principles being our breath, where we look, what we engage or how we move.

Here are the four stages of learning, be it any kind of learning. This could be learning to drive, learning to speak another language or learning yoga asanas.

1. *When we begin something, we are unconsciously incompetent, we're unaware of what we don't know.*

2. *When we start to learn something new, we become consciously incompetent, we become aware of what we don't know.*

3. *As we learn we become consciously competent, we know what we're doing but we must think about it.*

4. *Lastly, we become unconsciously competent, we can do something without thinking about it, like a skilled professional in their area of expertise.*

The beauty of Series One is that we can get to the point where we are unconsciously competent, knowing the order of postures without thinking about them. We can flow, breathe and enjoy. It's beautiful to watch a group of yogis moving from one posture to the next, it looks like a dance or maybe even a murmuration of starlings.

The First Principle
Ujjayi Breathing

The yogic breath has three names: Ocean breath, Victorious breath, or Ujjayi breath. That person with the loud breathing who you possibly thought was a little strange, isn't strange at all. That yogi or yogini is using the Ujjayi breathing technique in the correct way, it's a deep, slow, and sounded breath. To find it, imagine you're trying to steam up a mirror with your exhalation, open your mouth and breathe out heavily. Notice the constriction in your throat as you blow out air? Do the same again, but with your mouth closed. Can you hear it? Now breathe again but this time breathe both in, and out, through your nose keeping your mouth closed and with the same constriction in your throat. You should be able to both feel it and hear it.

Breathing in this way helps internalise our thoughts bringing our attention out of our head and into our body. The sound we make, helps block out any surrounding noise. It also helps us come into the here and now and most importantly, helps us concentrate on our postures in a meditative way. Lastly, Ujjayi breathing helps generate and maintain heat in the body. Ashtanga being Yang in nature, is a warm practice, attached to heat and sweat. Traditionally, it's advised to rub sweat back into the body as it's described as Prana or energy needing reabsorption. Ujjayi breathing is also the main breathing technique in the forth limb of Yoga, Pranayama.

The Second Principle

Bandhas

Bandhas are known as energy centres meaning 'lock' or 'seal'. They're non-anatomical energy centres of the body that can't be found in Westernised medical books. The mula bandha is at the base of the torso between the anus and the genitals at the perineum. The mula bandha is associated with the multi-layered set of pelvic floor muscles, which when contracted creates stability for the pelvic bowl and the spine that rises from it. When contracted, this Bandha helps us push into the floor in standing postures resulting in stability. Think both *Warrior One* and *Warrior Two*, both examples of postures being more effective when using our mula bandha.

To activate the mula bandha start by engaging the pelvic floor and imagine contracting the muscles you would use to stop the flow of urine, midstream. Aim to relax the muscles of the anus and genitals and instead isolate and draw up the perineum.

Our second bandha or 'lock' is called uddiyana bandha meaning 'upward flying' and is found at our core centre. It involves the contraction of the abdomen up and into the rib cage, so it's important to only switch this bandha on when we have an empty stomach. It's also associated with three muscles of the iliopsoas (hip). The psoas major, the less powerful psoas minor, and the iliacus muscle, when combined it is known as the iliopsoas and attaches the spine through the hips to the legs, primarily giving us the ability to walk. Uddiyana bandha helps us lift and rise, or 'fly'.

Maybe we want to jump back and forth on our mats during sun salutations or vinyasas? Crow pose is a good example of wanting 'lift and rise' using the help of uddiyana bandha and bringing our whole torso higher, although to start with there's more crashing onto our faces than actual flying! Switching this Bandha on during our practice helps us feel at ease, gives us more support, and helps our postures and movements feel lighter.

To activate the uddiyana bandha, pull in and lift the area behind the navel bringing the torso upwards; imagine the diaphragm, stomach and abdominal organs all lifting upwards creating a concavity in the belly at the same time, draw the navel back towards the spine.

The last of the Bandhas is our Jalandhara Bandha, our throat or chin lock. It's primarily in postures that require more attention to the breath whilst aiming to steady the nervous system, poses such as Padmasana (a cross legged or lotus seated pose), Dandasana (a straight legged, seated pose), and Salamba Sarvangasana (a shoulder stand). Jalandhara bandha, in some postures, can give us a feeling of being enclosed and possibly claustrophobic, especially postures whilst in a shoulder stand. Breathing becomes restricted, so concentrating and aiming to relax is good training if ever there are situation where there are too many people in a small environment or if we feel anxious or apprehensive.

To activate the jalandhara bandha bring the chin to the chest, and the chest to the chin, somewhere between the two ends of the collarbones. Doing this engages many muscles of the torso and the lower back.

The Third Principle
Drishti

Drishti in Sanskrit means 'gaze' or 'vision'. It's where we look during our practice, often explained as a 'place to rest one's eyes', and plays a part in our practice being a moving meditation, as well as directing energy in the direction we want it. Our drishti plays a huge part in balancing poses without concentrating on our gaze we risk face planting.

There are nine key Drishti places in Ashtanga Yoga:

1. The tip of the nose
2. The thumbs
3. The hands
4. The toes
5. The navel
6. Ajna Chakra (Third Eye)
7. Upwards toward the sky
8. Far to the left
9. Far to the right

Focusing helps us internalise our practice, increasing our ability to feel our way; it helps us balance and it helps us concentrate on what we're doing.

We may want to consider what and who we gaze at in everyday life. We often watch others and wish we could be like them, both on and off our mats, in turn driving ourselves to unfair comparisons. Many of us worry what others think of us. Our Drishti teaches us to look at what we're doing, it teaches us to avoid looking anywhere other than our intention; it also helps us focus, especially in arm balances where directing our attention helps the postures happen.

If we gaze at our Third Eye during meditation, we can choose to have our eyes open or closed. You might agree, the words 'place to rest one's eyes' feels calm and nurturing.

The Fourth and last Principle
Vinyasa

Vinyasa literally means movement with breath. During asanas we attach breath with movement to create what's called a Vinyasa flow. A Vinyasa is a short set of movements to include lengthening, flexing, extending, and stretching our muscles and fascia between specific postures. Vinyasas do four things; they separate postures from one to the next and they separate postures from the right side and the left side; they also help to maintain body temperature by keeping the body warm and lubricated and they keep the Prana moving and flowing. A rule of thumb is to breathe in when creating an upward movement and breathe out when creating a downward movement. I've learnt through experience that this doesn't always apply but mostly it's helpful. There are thirty-five Vinyasas between poses in *Series One*, add the Sun Salutations (warm up) and the number goes up to an incredible eighty-eight Vinyasas! Imagine if you commit to practising traditionally six days a week. That's a lot of lengthening, flexing, extending, twisting, and stretching as well as a lot of strength and 'planking' in Chaturanga Dandasana, not to mention a lot of sweat - which of course needs rubbing back in!

A 'Vinyasa' can be the name of an entire class.

There are many styles of yoga, and it can seem very confusing when choosing a class. Not all styles of yoga suit everyone. A *Vinyasa class* is the name given to a specific yoga class that involves using 'movement and breath'. It isn't a traditional class but instead relies on the creativity of the yoga instructor to link and flow postures from one pose to the next. Based on yang philosophy a vinyasa class works the muscles of the body whilst protecting joints.

Doing what feels good

At times, practitioners' question if some poses or movements are correct compared with how they may have practised in another class. Questioning if their wrist and forearm should be externally or internally rotated for instance during a dancers pose or where their feet should be pointing in a wheel pose. One teacher suggests it 'this way' and another teacher, 'that way'. I am influenced by, and believe in functional yoga, so in my opinion there is no perfect pose and no right pose away from a traditional practice, instead only the pose that feels good for us. Traditional poses in traditional classes do have set shapes and intentions, although I choose to support practitioners in feeling free to move and hold their bodies in ways that feel good and safe for them. You may have your wrist and forearm internally rotated, or externally rotated, you may have your feet straight, or turned out a little. My suggestion is always to try both and enjoy the one that feels good for you.

Have we become sticklers for wanting to do things right in the name of being correct, perfect or what's written in a book? Maybe we've forgotten to feel or trust our own guidance? Do we live in the confines of rules? Do we forget to listen to ourselves and our intuition? Do we need to let go, free things up, break a few rules and live a little on the edge?

'Sometimes I want a quiet life, other times I want to go a little bit f*cking Gatsby.'

- Atticus

Doing what feels good is far safer than aiming for the 'perfect aesthetic pose' whatever that is to us. It's tempting to want to achieve what we see others achieve or what we see on social media. A reminder here to never feel anything more than mild discomfort and never to feel pain. No pose is the perfect pose, just like life, other people's 'way' might not be our own. Knowing there is 'no way', just our own way makes yoga even more personal and very achievable.

When we're in the three key factors of posture, breathing and gaze we're said to be in a state of *Tristhana* which means we're in a position of purifying the body and mind. The Tristhana method sets an Ashanga style of yoga apart from other styles. A focused energy believed to be the gateway to the spiritual side of yoga and a doorway to self-discovery.

Practising Asanas with bare feet allows us to move our bodies as nature intended whilst keeping us connected and rooted to the ground. Very humbling and the perfect excuse to paint one's toenails pretty colours!

We have two-hundred-and-six bones in our body, over six-hundred muscles, and over two-hundred-and-fifty joints! We're so incredibly different with different skeletal structures and unique joint socket shapes. Because of this, asanas, especially during a Yin yoga practice can look completely different from one person to another and that's just fine and just how it should be.

An Ashtanga style of yoga is practised with the muscles engaged. It predominantly builds strength, balance and core stability. A Yin style of yoga is practised with the muscles relaxed. It predominantly creates wider ranges of movement, flexibility and exercises the joints, facia, ligaments, and tendons.

The Chinese Taoist philosophy is earth honouring and feminine based. Tao means 'the way' that is, the way of nature.

We are surrounded by Yin and Yang. Up and down, black, and white, tall, and short, hot, and cold. Yin is the opposite of Yang and Yang is the opposite of Yin, however, within a yoga practice there are no absolutes. Classes may be named 'Yin' or 'Yang', however, there are always elements of Yin in a Yang practice and vice-versa. They are different in their approach although both circulate subtle energy named 'Prana' or 'Chi' via the 'Nadis' (also called Meridians). These energetic lines are believed to hold a chemical named hyaluronic acid, which according to new meridian theory is held or encapsulated by water. Each one gram of hyaluronic acid binds sixty-one grams of water. Hyaluronic acid chains or molecules are continually being produced by the body when stimulated within the connective tissue, and supports every structure of the human body.

Hyaluronic acid is widely and increasingly used in face creams to help the skin absorb and retain water making it appear hydrated and glowing.

Two years after learning, practising, and sharing an Ashtanga style of yoga, I decided to study Yin yoga with the incredibly knowledgeable Paul Grilley, who in 2000, extracted the slow and long held postures of this ancient shamanic tradition of the Chinese Taoist philosophy and created classes based on them and their benefits to the western world. According to Paul Grilley and his mentor and guru, the late Dr Hiroshi Motoyama, a renowned Japanese scientist and Shinto priest, believed (and created scientific research to demonstrate), that the water rich channels of the fascia are in fact the meridian lines of our body.

Yin yoga is an effective way to increase the production of hyaluronic acid as it targets connective tissue such as the ligaments, tendons, facia, and bones in passive poses that can be held anywhere between three and fifteen minutes.

'Create motion for lotion'

According to the Chinese practice of acupuncture the Meridians are stimulated using needles to awaken the Chi (energy), bringing mental or physical health benefits. Meridians (or Nadis) travel and intertwine through the whole body, through the connective tissue, around bones, joints, and organs. Therefore, one might have an acupuncture needle inserted into a Meridian line at one end of the body, even though the problem lies at the other.

Yin is unique in two ways; in that it's practised with the muscles relaxed and secondly that postures are held for a longer period. When muscles are relaxed, our joints are put into a position of vulnerability; with this, the joint is stressed and exercised. As we hold postures and mentally 'let go', we invite stored tension to dissipate. Putting the joints under stress makes them stronger. This is an integral part of Yin yoga. Paul Grilley has played a big part in developing this slow-paced style of yoga. He and his wife, Suzee, share their learning and practice with thousands around the world. A Yin practice is slow, deep, and nurturing.

In the Western world, we sit at our desks, sit in our cars, and sit on our sofas, we become stuck in one shape. If we do that often enough, we start to lose mobility, especially in our lower spines. Sitting in one shape for hours, day after day, isn't healthy for us. Yin yoga, through its philosophy, invites the body to increase its range of movement and return to its natural state and functionality as it's intended.

I'm opposed to a yoga asana practice based on aesthetics, instead, I'm aiming to look deeper into our unique skeletal structures. We just need to look at Instagram for instance, to see photo after photo of yogis creating crazy pretzel shapes and deep backbends. These may be hypermobile individuals or professional dancers with genetically open hips, spaced vertebrae and elongated muscles and fascia, but for a typical yogi this is not the true essence of yoga and not what yoga intended. Yoga asanas exercise the body and create a feeling within the body, irrelevant of what that body aesthetically looks like. A deeper asana pose for some is an individual looking for the same feeling as someone else in a shallower pose, proving we're all so different. Unfortunately, many of us in the Western world are impressed both with aesthetics as well as physicality, which boasts 'deeper', 'stronger', 'faster' and 'harder' regimes, enabling us to see and measure what we believe to be a 'success'. In a class someone may be uber bendy and another quite tight, yet it's the feeling we're searching for, and not the shape. We must learn to put the ego to one side, to enable us to have an honest practice and honour our bodies. Different shapes, same or similar feelings.

Just because one person can get deeper into a pose doesn't mean it's better, it's just different. We must continually remind ourselves that we're aiming for a feeling not an image.

Paul Grilley throws out the rule book, which I love because by nature, I enjoy breaking rules. Instead of too much instruction, he invites us to create autonomy and connect to our bodies, feeling our own way. Many of us find ourselves looking for a formula or directions rather than listening to our own body, mind, and intuition.

He reminds me constantly that there is no right way or wrong way, just the practitioner's way. He has made me less likely to want to adjust someone in a posture but instead create autonomy through conversation about what they can feel and if that feeling is a good feeling. He has taught me about compression in the human skeleton and explained why one person can comfortably come into a seated lotus or back bend for instance, whilst another will never comfortably sit or bend into that position through their entire life, no matter how often or how long they practice.

A Yin practice works deeper into the body. To watch a Yin practice, you could be excused for thinking it's easy. Oh no! Yin is soft and long and dreamy but far from a push over.

I was first introduced to a Yin class the day before my training started in India. I loved every minute of it. In fact, I panicked and thought I may have travelled halfway around the world, *again* (this time in the opposite direction) and put myself on another wrong course. However, after asking a few questions I learnt that most, if not all, modern yoga training starts with Ashtanga learning. If you asked me why, I'd say because Ashtanga has a structure just as Sri Pattabhi Jois intended. When we have a structure, we have a solid base to systematise and learn an outcome, which can be measured and accredited wherever it's taught and shared in the world. Like many things we learn, the start becomes the foundation for what we learn to follow.

A Yin practice is much freer, in that there is no perfect pose, no right way and no structure. We aim to find the right pose for our own body before completely letting go, allowing muscles to relax and leaving joints to feel exposed.

The whole practice is long and slow. Vulnerability is key for the body to become stronger. Yin postures help to decompress the spine, elongate the fascia, exercise our joints, ligaments, and tendons, and increase the production of that all-important hyaluronic acid.

How is slow good? Imagine a dentist wanting to move a tooth. A tooth is cold and hard, like bone, it can therefore be seen as Yin in nature. If the dentist wiggled the tooth back and forth and back and forth to move it, the tooth would eventually fall out. If on the other hand he put a brace on the tooth and every so often tightened the brace, little by little, over months, the tooth would move and ease slowly and gently into place. Paul Grilley explains that the Yin way of practising yoga affects the body in very much the same way.

Over hours, weeks, and months, we open the body, and as we do, we free up our minds with it. What goes on in the mind, goes on in the body. What goes on in the body, goes on in the mind. Yin is an amazing form of yoga that works deep into our physical, energetic and mental sheaths (or Kosha's), whilst also giving us time, space and awareness to clear and calm our minds bringing us to a state of wisdom and bliss.

If you enjoy sports that are faster, harder, quicker, or stronger, you'll benefit from a Yin practice. In fact, any time we sit on the ground, our bodies find shapes which replicate Yin postures.

Be a little Yin, be a little Yang.

Shavasana

Shavasana, sometimes spelt Savasana, is the last pose practised at the end of each class. Shavasana translated means 'corpse pose', and is deemed by many to be the most challenging of poses as some find it hard to relax, give themselves to the ground and not fidget. It's a fully conscious pose, laying on our backs with our arms inwardly or externally rotated and our legs slightly apart. Make Shavasana your own by possibly bringing a block or bolster under your knees helping take any pressure off the lower back, placing a cushion under your neck or laying under a blanket. Putting our attention on the out breath helps settle both our bodies and minds in this ultimate pose which helps us release physically, mentally, and emotionally. Please don't be tempted to skip Shavasana. In fact, the more likely you are to want to roll your mat up and creep away towards your daily chores, the more likely your body and mind probably needs it. Embrace Shavasana, learn to let go, give yourself to the ground and allow a peaceful state to enter your being.

SOS Yoga Mat!

Before we move onto the fourth limb of Patanjali's Yoga, it's worth sharing here how useful and resourceful our yoga mats can be. Whenever or wherever I travel, I take one or two of my mats with me; one heavier more substantial mat, and another lighter mat, should I want to go walking into the 'wilderness'. Firstly, we can practice on them, we can also use them to literally lay on and relax and thirdly we can use them when we want to separate ourselves from whatever flooring, base or place of rest has been offered.

My daughter Ellie and I decided to have a week away. I've always believed in spending individual time with my children, be it a day out, a weekend, or week away. All relationships are unique and each one, I feel, should be recognised, and enjoyed separately and individually.

We were heading for Cornwall to a beautiful shepherd's hut sat high on a hill overlooking St. Ives. It's a long drive, especially if you drive from Leicestershire down the M1 towards Northampton before realising you're driving in the wrong direction. Dean insists 99.999% of the population would drive down the M5 towards Birmingham – hey ho, I like an adventure.

'I'm so sorry' the lady said. 'We're full. Oh, hang on,' she said. 'I could let you stay in what we call the Events Shed, if you don't mind that is? I don't usually let people sleep in there as it's used as a meeting place for everyone, but since you have a thing for sheds, I'd like to help you'.

'Thank you so much, we'd love to!' I replied excitedly 'Fancy that!'

It was a night I will never forget. We laughed so hard we didn't know what to do with ourselves. It was a gin tasting evening (I don't even like gin!). The idea was to flavour gin with herbs, berries and flowers from the venues 'meadow gardens', a questionable area behind a barn, with varied and random engineering and car parts from various decades. We were invited to drink our own, and taste everyone else's too, which turned out to be quite a sociable endeavour. Later that evening we needed to visit the bathroom. We were directed to cross a field and go into a specific shed or summer house which had a toilet and washroom to the rear. The washroom consisted of a portable toilet and a hose pipe having been poked through a hole in the wall for showering and hand washing. It wasn't a problem at all apart from it was filthy and worse, it smelled like a pack of wild animals had been sleeping in it. On leaving we must have forgotten to close the doors simply because we were both utterly wasted.

At the end of the evening and after drinking copious amounts of gin, (It started to taste very nice!), we were led by our host in the dark to our 'Event Shed'. It was a stormy night and raining hard, and it quickly transpired it was the very same shed - having recently been visited by sheep! A very drunk mother and daughter and our host, stood staring at abundant amounts of sheep poo and glistening urine!

I called a friend while our hostess went off to fetch a bucket and mop. At the same time tiny drops of rainwater were dripping in through the roof. My friend was raising her voice, 'It's disgusting Manda! You need to leave right now!' Which of course added to the hilarity and made us laugh more because we were completely sh*t faced. There was nothing I could do and nowhere to go. We were literally standing in a shed in the middle of a field in a storm. I remember being unbelievably relieved when I remembered we'd brought in our yoga mats.

I wrote this poem the following day. 'Ha ha ha - That's exactly how it was Mum', Ellie said.

There's something I didn't mention,
It wasn't a mistake.
It was actually my intention,
Because I like to make fun,
Of the things I've experienced,
(But I don't like causing offence).
You see,
I booked this Airbnb,
For my beautiful clever daughter and me.
It was to spend an evening,
With 'people of the land', shall I say.

Oohhh , the evening went well,
Until they mentioned things like,
'Our son and visitors sometimes sleep with the animals'
And,
'We don't have a washing machine'.
Ha-ha, that's funny.
Er, no - it is not!

It started to rain,
And
I started to scratch,
I'm not a drinker, but that night I drank too much.
I felt fuzzy and dizzy.
And a little bit squiffy.
But never one to hold a grudge.

At the end of the night,
We were led over a field with a torch,
To our overnight 'people of the land'
Shed with a bed.

It wasn't good.
You see the lack of the washing machine thing,
Clicked in my head,
And the smell of black Labradors,
Coming from the bed,
Made our senses soar!

(To the point where we wanted to be sick).

We felt nauseous and itchy all over.

There was a Porta Loo too,
With stenches of poo,
And there was a window that was completely missing.
So,
The wind blew the dirty curtain,
Making the dog fumes diffuse the pre-storm air.

I scratched more but we laughed
even more than you'd expect.
But then,
It got even worse,
Because when we stepped inside,
We slipped on sheep shite,
And the lady said
'Oh no, I'm so sorry'.

She fetched a mop and poked it,
In the direction of my Cath Kidston luggage bags.
And something inside me,
Died.

But
It got worse still,
Because to top it,
It wasn't just shit.
The sheep had literally,
Pissed over the entire floor.
T'was literally dripping down the door,
Yes!
We could see it,
In the light of the moon,
Through the missing window,
With the maroon,
Dirty curtain.

Luckily, I had a thought,
And remember what we'd brought.
Whilst wanting to add to the urine problem with laughter.
So,
We stripped off the bed,
And placed out yoga mats instead,
And
Our sweet-smelling sleeping bags.

Then sprayed perfume over the
Macerated floor.
Phew!

Yes, we slept with nuances of sheep poo,
T'was like sleeping in a filthy zoo!
But being 'over the limit',
What was our choice?
What could we do?

My alarm was set for 4am,
The alcohol had just about worn off by then,
And we tip-toed across the field,
Shutting our car doors,
At...
Exactly the same time!
Skills!

...Airbnb
We apologise
As
We ran away. We escaped!

We felt crazy and daring - but dirty.

Thank Goodness
McDonald's opened at 6.30!

-   Manda

I contacted the host the following day.
She kindly said our stay was 'on the house'.

Take your mat wherever you go.
You never know when you'll need it.

The Fourth Limb of Yoga

Pranayama
Extension of the breath or life force

By the time we get to the end of our physical asana practice, our bodies feel invigorated, calm, and open, and we have a better ability to sit without feeling restless. Pranayama refers to breathing exercises which clear the physical and emotional obstacles in our body. Pranayama is the fourth limb of Patanjali's Eight Limbed Path and is mostly practised whilst sitting crossed legged or in Padmasana (Lotus Position). Ujjayi breathing is a fundamental part of each Pranayama session, starting, ending, and connecting one Pranayama technique to the next.

Traditionally an individual can begin to learn Pranayama once they have mastered each individual pose in Chikitsa (or Primary Series), it's here you can sense a feeling of the journey of yoga.

We can live for weeks without food, we can live for days without water, yet we can only live for minutes without breath.

Yogis believe, that as humans we are more likely to live a longer life if we breathe deeply and slowly. Pranayama is a practice of controlling and regulating the breath. This includes inhalation, exhalation, and breath retention.

The three Sanskrit words used in Pranayama breathing are Pooraka (Inhalation), Rechaka (Exhalation) and Kumbhaka (Breath retention). It's during Kumbhaka that Yogis believe to be of most benefit, as it nourishes our Prana, or energy. Of course, we don't have to remember the Sanskrit names but by being aware we can increase our focus.

Box breathing is a simple and effective way to experience Pooraka, Rechaka and Kumbhaka. It helps quieten the mind and nourish our bodies in Prana. To do this, breathe in slowly for the count of four, hold your breath for the count of four, breathe out for the count of four, and then hold for the count of four before inhaling again.

The diaphragm is associated with uddiyana bandha, and enables us to breathe. It's a thin muscle that separates our abdomen from our chest and creates a vacuum which pulls air into the lungs. Think of the diaphragm as a lift in a tall building, lowering, and contracting as we inhale whilst expanding our lungs, then returning to a dome shape as we exhale.

There are many different breathing techniques that can be used to calm, invigorate, add heat, cool, and stimulate the body. Searching Pranayama on YouTube is possibly the best way to get an idea of what Pranayama breathing techniques look like to include Bhastrika (bellows breath) which invigorates and heats the body, and Sitali or Sitkari which both cool the body.

Nadi Shodhana

We have two nostrils and one nose, and the air meets at the top, yet, during some Pranayama breathing techniques we use the division of our nostrils to bring our attention to each side of the body, separating the left from the right, warm from cool, sun from moon, introversion from extroversion and energy from tranquillity. It's a clever way to prepare ourselves, be it to invigorate ourselves before a busy day or before an Ashtanga class or calm ourselves before bedtime or before a yin class.

The Right Nostril

Surya Bedhana meaning 'sun pierce' are the words given to the warming Pranayama breath work, through the right nostril. The right nostril is connected to the Pingala Nadi and controls the vital processes of the body and increases pranic energy. Right nostril breathing is believed to revitalise the body, increase the efficiency of the digestive system, and boost the nervous system, especially the sympathetic nervous system which is associated with the fight or flight psychological response. It is associated with the sun, masculinity, physical energy, and extroversion as well as helping the body feel energised and warm.

The Left Nostril

Chandra Badhana meaning 'moon pierce' are the words given to cooling Pranayama breath work through the left nostril. The left nostril is connected to Chandra Nadi (also called Ida Nadi) and controls mental processes of the body as well as being associated with the moon, femininity, introversion, calm, and coolness. Breathing through the left nostril is believed to help us simmer down, relax, and sleep better.

Vishnu Mudra is the correct hand shape to help achieve single, or alternate, nostril breathing named Nadi Shodhana

How to create Vishnu Mudra

Using your right hand, bend your index finger and middle finger towards your palm, leaving your thumb, ring and little finger straight. Place your thumb over your right nostril. Let go, and then place your ring finger over your left nostril. You're now ready for alternate nostril breathing. I find it hard to straighten my ring finger (too much hairdressing), in this mudra, so instead I use my thumb and little finger.

Mudras are specific hand gestures created to facilitate the flow of energy or Prana. The word 'Mudra' is a Sanskrit word that literally means 'hand gesture'. Think of hand gestures as yoga asanas for the hands that not only exercise the hands but also hold or re-direct energy through the body. During mudras we bend, press, cross, extend or touch our fingers with other fingers. By doing so we alter the flow of energy or Prana/Chi through acupuncture points which in turn stimulate specific areas of the brain and help bring about balance and wellbeing.

Our right nostril is energetically associated with our body's heating energy, symbolised by the 'sun' and the syllable 'HA'. Our left nostril, with our body's cooling energy, symbolised by the 'moon' and the syllable 'THA'. Many of us, due to the way we think and behave, are in conflict physically and mentally, which is believed over time to disquiet the mind and risk us suffering from stress, worry, anxiety or dis-of-ease.

Using alternate nostril breathing singularly, or alternately, in Nadi Shodhana brings good results. We can create balance and harmony by mindfully breathing through both nostrils, or we can breathe only through the left nostril if we want to feel cool, calm and introverted which is useful if we've had a hectic day and want to calm ourselves down. Breathing through our right nostril if we want to feel warm and energised is especially good if we feel tired but want some energy to keep going.

Hatha Yoga

The goal of traditional Hatha Yoga, integrates and harmonises 'HA' and 'THA' for happiness and health. The purpose of these two breaths is to create balance by 'warming' a 'cool' body and 'cooling' a 'warm' body. A yoga class described as 'Hatha' will typically involve a set of physical postures (yoga poses) and breathing techniques. These are usually practised slowly and with more static postures than a Vinyasa flow or Ashtanga class.

Isn't it funny how we breathe all day long, yet we don't pay much attention to it? Learning to breathe properly is beneficial for all sorts of health and wellbeing reasons. It also holds the answer if we feel nervous, anxious, or scared, especially in situations where we're the centre of attention, possibly just before a speech or presentation. I experienced my breath or lack of it, that morning in San Diego when my heart started to beat so fast, and I panicked and began to lose my breath. My whole being went into a stress response. The more we panic the more we feel as though we can't breathe and the more, we feel we can't breathe, the more we panic and so on.

It could be likened to physically running up a hill. If we run fast enough and hard enough, we soon get an oxygen debt which results in us, at some point needing to stop. That 'heart pumping' feeling we get is similar to when we're nervous, panicked or anxious.

Using our breath to inhale and exhale deeply and slowly brings our breath back to its normal state until we feel back to our resting heart rate and fully recovered.

If we're about to publicly speak for instance and we're nervous, our heart can race in exactly the same way, resulting in us feeling agitated, irritable, and wanting to run away! We're putting our bodies under stress and experiencing the same physicality as if we've just ran up a hill. At some point in our speech or conversation, usually near the beginning, we are forced to stop and find our breath. I've found that if I breathe deeply and slowly before starting to speak in the first place, I find I'm in a calmer state and less likely to become breathless. Breathing mindfully beforehand, helps us calm our bodies and minds whilst adding oxygen or energy to our body, we then become more relaxed. Like all habits, the more we experience something with added insight, the easier it gets.

Learning and using Pranayama breathing helped me to confidently stand up and deliver the eulogy at my mother's funeral. I would never have thought I would ever be able to do such a thing. Yoga supported me.

The Fifth Limb of Yoga

Pratyahara
Withdrawal of the senses

Pratyahara is the fifth limb in the Eight Limbed Path of Patanjali's yoga, and often referred to as the rainbow limb, bridging and facilitating the gap between the body and the mind. Here we have the opportunity to work deeper, from the physical and energetic layers towards our mind, emotions, wisdom and bliss. Pratyahara means 'withdrawing the self from all negative forms of nourishment' or 'withdrawal of the senses'.

Pratyahara helps us make the transition into meditation by noticing and settling our unruly senses.

This isn't just about sitting down and closing our eyes but closing and dulling down our hearing, taste, touch, and smell. During Pratyahara we're starting to internalise, putting all our attention on our inner world only. By doing this we can get an insight into what's going on and aim to create knowledge about ourselves, how we're feeling without the sensations brought to us from our senses and the opinions we hold about them.

When we practice breath work, followed by dulling down our senses, it is recommended that we sit cross legged or in Padmasana with a straight spine whilst breathing naturally and deeply, possibly focusing on an area between our eyebrows called our Third Eye or Ajna Chakra. It has taken me a while not to feel as though I'm screwing my face up but have found that focusing on the Third Eye once relaxed, brings a sense of internalisation and even escapism.

You may find that sitting cross legged and upright is still uncomfortable. Don't be afraid to lie down, lean against a wall or pop a cushion under your buttocks which helps tilt the pelvis forward and for many, makes sitting much more comfortable, but aim to keep your spine straight. Sitting comfortably this way can take a long time to accomplish, hence the physical benefits of yoga asanas.

Padmasana, or Lotus Position, is the traditional shape to sit in. Why? Because when we sit in full Lotus, we have a large surface area connected to the ground. This position allows our spines to be long and straight, our bones to sit on the floor and our hips to open. Over time it promotes good posture, keeps our joints and ligaments flexible in the knees and feet and increases awareness and attentiveness.

Guess what? I've been teaching for over two years and practising yoga for ten, and I still can't sit in a Lotus pose. My ego desperately wishes I could, because then I might look more like a yogini on my Instagram posts and less like a child sitting in morning assembly. The fundamental standing poses of *Series One* concentrate on opening the hips, which will help with this seated posture along with many seated hip opening asanas, however, for some we will never be able to sit in this position as the insertions of our bones into our joint sockets won't allow us. If we are tight through the fascia, muscles, tendons, and ligaments, we may find over time and with patience, that we open up and one day find ourselves in this beautiful pose, however if we can feel bone on bone at our hip insertions then we will only damage ourselves over time by continually trying. Bones pressing on bones is something we need to be aware of. When a bone presses onto another bone, it means *we're done*. It demonstrates that our unique skeleton has come to a place where we can go no further. No matter how hard we practice, how regularly we practice or how much we breathe into the posture, our bodies won't budge. An X-ray could visually prove this, an easier way is to experiment by mindfully feeling our way.

Here it's very important to note the difference between what feels like *tension* and what feels like *compression*. If we feel tension, we can safely and over time continue opening our hips and look forward to the day we can sit like this. However, our femur, the longest bone in the body, doesn't always want to sit at the angle that Lotus pose requests. If we force compressed bones into Lotus pose, we are doing more harm than good. It's worth adding here also, that many knee injuries are caused by those trying to force their legs into a lotus position before their body (hips) are open enough and ready for it.

There is a field close to where we live, I've named it 'My Field of Dreams'. It isn't a particularly special field, and you wouldn't guess where it is, however, I was walking around the outside of it during the long hot summer last year, and was suddenly drawn to sit down on the ground and stay a while. I made a point of sitting in the same spot maybe four times a week and just - be. I'm finding it hard to describe what this did for me, but it felt quite amazing.

Pratyahara helps us remove our minds from day-to-day noise, bright lights, interferences, world news and all the other things that fill our heads. It helps us become mindful of our surroundings, the impressions we take in, and the associations we keep. We live in a world where we're constantly being advertised to and 'enticed'. Have you noticed when you search for something in Google and the next minute it shows up on your Facebook feed? How dare they! Pratyahara helps us identify and reduce or abolish what we don't want to focus on, instead we can choose to walk away, switch off or un-plug.

Many of us can reduce the amount we eat, drink and even people we don't want to spend our time with, but we are not aware that we too can reduce what our eyes see, and our ears hear. Pratyahara makes us aware of the 'rubbish' in the form of sensations and impressions we continually watch, listen, or are subjected to, that we'd benefit without. Imagine sitting beside *your* field. The sun is warm and glowing, the breeze is soft and comforting. You're sitting cross legged, leaning against a tree or upright in Padmasana, whilst bringing your attention to your breath and gazing out towards the horizon; and then, when you're ready, feeling yourself slowly coming into Pratyahara or *withdrawal of the senses*. Bringing your focus towards your

Third Eye and gradually letting each part of your body become relaxed and withdrawn from the outside world.

Pratyahara refers to controlling our senses and highlighting the sensory overload that we often unconsciously put on ourselves. Are we spending time with the wrong people? Are we getting too much negative stimulation? Are we tempted by the wrong foods? Have we lost control over our senses and impulses? Pratyahara helps in rightly managing our senses, it prepares our minds and helps us gain control over our distractions, leading us to greater focus in preparation for meditation.

Practice Yoga asana
Use Pranayama for breath control
Sit in meditation, aiming to reduce your senses

The Sixth Limb of Yoga

Dharana
To concentrate, maintain or hold

The aim of this sixth limb is to focus on one of our senses only, by doing this we are separating the noise and disturbances of our life and minds. We could concentrate on our breath, a mantra, an object, or a specific part of our body.

A mandala is Sanskrit meaning 'Circle or 'Sacred circle'. It's a geometric design that holds a great deal of symbolism in many cultures. Mandalas are believed to represent different aspects of the universe and are used as instruments to focus upon during meditation. They emit and attract positive energy. They are also symbols of prayer particularly in China, Japan, and Tibet.

Whilst training in India, we had meditation sessions most evenings where we were asked to stare into the flame of a candle. I found it extremely difficult to do and spent most of my time wondering if the doctors and surgeons at Moorfields Eye Hospital would recommend staring into such a bright light, to which I don't know the answer. Maybe I wasn't ready for Dharana? In fact, I don't believe I was. I considered it a bit of a waste of time being the Pitta, A-type, Red personality that I am and preferring to choose to do something more 'useful' instead.

A Pitta, A-type, Red personality can be described as a determined, focused, driven person who has high energy and often looks for the next thing on the agenda, finding meditation challenging.

Traditionally we wouldn't move to the next limb until we've mastered the last. Should you find Dharana too demanding, step back a limb. There's plenty of time.

We rush through life, rarely or never stopping to notice what's happening within us. When we're anxious or tense, we may notice that our bodies have aches and pains, we hold our breath or sweat more than is natural for us. By noticing, stopping, and taking time to be still, we can have a conversation with ourselves. We can teach our minds to reduce the 'noise' and the internal chatter, whilst we listen to what's really going on.

I remember a friend, and fellow yogini, telling me that she went to an event where the teacher suggested they all meditate whilst putting all their attention on a strawberry. My friend allegedly spent the whole time trying not to laugh and thought the entire process hilarious. I can relate to such outbursts. But the thing here is; the teacher was teaching the correct concept. She was sharing the magic of Dharana and facilitating the journey into the deep delights of meditation.

I've come to identify that it's basically down to where we are. Down to whether the practitioner is physically and/or mentally ready, which includes me. When I say that, it may be that we're not in the right place yet, or it may be that we're not in the right place *today*. If we're finding it hard to focus, it may be because we've not yet invested, or have enough evidence to believe in meditation or the eight limbs; or it may be that this month, this week or today we feel fidgety in our bodies or erratic in our thoughts. If so, Dharana becomes too encompassing and too much of a challenge – in which case step back a limb or do more asana.

Those who aren't interested in meditation, might think
you are a little crazy. On the other hand, it may be that they
can't relax themselves, so can't relate.

Let's use a pebble as our focal point. I say a pebble because it's on my Bliss List and my favourite word as a child. The thought of a pebble engages me before I even start. With that, I suggest you do the same and use something from your Bliss List. Why? Because it will involve your interests or passions. If we feel rested and comfortable whilst sitting, we can start to breathe long and slow. We become conscious of that pebble; the pebble is all we see, and all we need to see. We can observe the pebble, its shape, size, texture, and colour. We can imagine where the pebble came from or where it might end up. As long as we focus on the pebble only and what it relates to.

What does this do exactly? It brings us into conscious meditation, so we're thinking about what we're doing bringing us into awareness. Whilst we're focusing on the pebble, we aren't focusing on anything else. Not our busy day, not other people and not our wants and needs. We're consciously competent, we're aware of what we're doing and concentrating on the act.

You can choose to focus on a plant, a picture, a leaf, a book cover, a photo of Kevin Costner ... even? Instead, you might want to close your eyes. The concentration we acquire through the practice of Dharana seeps into other areas of our life enabling us to focus, think and even listen with more intent. Off the mat we can definitely use this professionally or when someone we love is talking to us and requires our full attention.

Practising Dharana can create space in our minds and give our minds a much-needed rest.

I've found that over the past couple of years of teaching the more practitioners relax through asanas, the more we collectively enjoy periods of short meditation, be it that it's just moments at the end of a class.

Practice Yoga asana
Use Pranayama for breath control
Sit in meditation aiming to reduce your senses
Concentrate on one sense, item or thought

The Seventh Limb of Yoga

Dhyana
'Glimpsing the Soul'

Dhyana is the seventh limb in the Eight Limbed Path of Patanjali's Yoga and here we go into complete and uninterrupted meditation. Here we become unconsciously competent at meditation.

Practising meditation is just like practising yoga asanas in that the more we do, the better we become. We can sit in meditation for fifteen seconds and if that becomes pleasant, we can try thirty seconds and so on. Accepting there is no rush is part of the yoga process. Dhyana is a place where we get to glimpse our soul, the space between our thoughts. It's here we find our own possibilities and meet our own wisdom.

Mediation isn't about force or struggle. It's about least effort. Imagine filling a glass jar with river water and shaking it. The water would be murky and filled with debris, but if you put that jar on a table and left it alone for a little while. All the activity, the sand, silt, and particles would settle to the bottom. Allowing the water to clear. Your mind works in the same way. Every day we are overloaded with eighty thousand thoughts; these thoughts can be overwhelming. If we allow the thoughts to just be and bring our awareness to the present moment. Eventually the jumble of our lives will settle, and we are able to see more clearly.

- Deepak Chopra

Our busy Westernised lifestyle and beliefs don't sit well with Dhyana. Many of us don't get this far believing we're completely wasting our time or not accomplishing very much. We put so much value on being busy that we often share with others how busy we are, and in return they share with us, how busy they are! Only patience and experience in meditation will allow us to know and understand its benefits.

Can we imagine sitting, without an alarm or time frame and let ourselves drift into deep mediation? Unfortunately many of us can't process that thought due to our frantic lives and busy diaries.

> *'You should sit in meditation for twenty minutes every day unless you're too busy; then you should sit for an hour.'*
> *- Zen Proverb*

What needs to happen, to enable us to benefit from this powerful limb?
What do we need to change or start to change?
What are we prepared to replace to make time?
How will we know we've made a good choice?

Here, we won't be thinking 'hey-I'm meditating! It'll be something we slip into spontaneously. I'm smiling here as I remember at twelve years old, sitting cross legged on my burgundy coloured bedroom carpet, meditating, right there next to my stack of disco lights.

When we want calm and peace – meditate
When we need to clear our minds – meditate
When we're looking for answers – meditate

Practice Yoga asana
Use Pranayama for breath control
Sit in meditation aiming to reduce your senses
Concentrate on one sense, item or thought
Gently separate yourself from your thoughts

The Eighth Limb of Yoga

Samadhi
Unification of mind

It's here we reach the end of Patanjali's Eight Limbed Path.
This is where complete integration of all eight limbs takes
place. The Sanskrit word 'Samadhi' means 'concentration' or
'unification of mind', it also means 'bliss' or 'enlightenment'.

Samadhi is said to be the highest form of cognitive ecstasy
and where we enter the deepest layer or Kosha of our being.

We have travelled through the physical body, the energetic
body, the mental and emotional layers to our inner wisdom.
Here we're in a state of bliss having travelled to the centre of
our *onion*.

Along our path of the eight limbs, we have learned ways to
deal with our world, understanding right living or ethical rules;
things we would benefit from if we did or didn't do. We've
moved our bodies resulting in stillness and connected with our
breath. We've removed external stimuli, focused our minds,
and sat deep in meditation. When we can sit in meditation
without the distractions and interruptions of the outside world,
we're ready for the highest state of Samadhi. Here, there is
said to be no separation between meditating, the process of
mediating and the object of meditation. In Samadhi we sit
completely still. We are fully unified within the eight limbs of
yoga.

The ultimate goal of yoga is called Kaivalya which means
'solitude' and 'isolation' or 'alone isolated'. We become aware
(conscious) of our soul (*Purusha*) becoming separate from
matter (*Prakriti*). Kaivalya brings us to a place of complete
awareness, understanding and supreme wisdom leading to
liberation.

Some practitioners may be in Samadhi for a while, others may slip in and out. I'm not sure if I've arrived this far in my practice yet and if I have, it has been brief. It's worth saying here that Samadhi isn't about floating away into la-la land, it's about approaching the life we have in front of us with absolute wisdom and purity.

The Eight Limbed Path is potentially a lifelong practice. We remind ourselves here to remain patient and to follow the limbs as they unfold as our thoughts, emotions, worries, memories, and desires are cleansed or conquered. We enter what's called *Ananda*, meaning bliss. At this time, we view the culmination of practicing all the other limbs of yoga bringing us to an understanding of knowing and feeling that everything is interconnected.

I know I've changed in many ways through personal development, learning and yoga. The eight limbs offer us a way forward and through this learning I feel less afraid of saying so when I don't understand something. I'm less competitive and feel far less involved in the lives of others, choosing to step back and concentrate on the bigger picture of life. The eight limbs of yoga have brought me support, a way forward and a sense of belonging. I feel calmer, quieter and I'd say, more content.

Practice Yoga asana
Use Pranayama for breath control
Sit in meditation aiming to reduce your senses
Concentrate on one sense, item or thought
Gently separate yourself from your thoughts
Integrate fully

Part Three

The Chakras
Balancing Energy

The Chakras were first mentioned in the Vedas some five thousand years ago; there is a lot to learn! Simplified, they connect to the *layers*, or *Koshas* of the body via nadis. Nadis are the channels that carry prana, namely our subtle energy. This energy travels through the seven main energy 'wheels' or 'vortexes' stacked along and above our spines. These energy epicentres are our Chakras. We aim to have a balanced Chakra system.

Energy channels are called Nadis by Indian yogis,
or Meridians by Chinese Daoists.

Daoism and Taoism are the same thing
The only difference is the spelling

As an accredited life coach, I'd like to share my interest in the Chakra system, as whatever your beliefs, using the information of the Chakras brings us greater self-awareness. When we have greater awareness, we have information to take action, change and appreciate our lives on a deeper physical, psychological and spiritual level.

A balanced Chakra system can bring us personal growth and transformational healing. Yoga philosophy teaches us to balance our Chakra system with the foods we eat, the poses we hold, meditation, sound, colour, chanting, crystals and scents. The chakra system focuses on our energetic body and the affect it has on our emotional and physical wellbeing.

Our Chakra system can be hard to understand, to simplify and explain how it works, I'd like you to imagine a garden hosepipe. Imagine you bought a hose but left it outside. One day, you try and use it but notice it's blocked. Dirt has made its way into the hose and stopped the water flowing. You can't poke a stick into the end of the pipe so instead you move your way up and down the hose, bending and flexing it, until the blockages clear and the water starts to flow.

Blockages within our Chakras are called granthis of which there are three kinds. Pronounced 'gruntees'. By balancing our chakras it is believed we can release these strong blockages and knots and create balance and harmony.

Here's a list below of the seven Chakras including their simple mantra:

- **Root Chakra** - Muladhara - 'I am'
- **Sacral Chakra -** Svadhisthana - 'I feel'
- **Solar Plexus Chakra** - Manipura - 'I do'
- **Heart Chakra** - Anahata - 'I love'
- **Throat Chakra** - Vishuddha - 'I talk'
- **Third Eye Chakra** - Ajna - 'I see
- **Crown Chakra** - Sahasrara - 'I understand'

What if our Chakras are unbalanced? We could also ask 'what if *we* feel unbalanced?' Either way, if we don't feel as grounded, confident, open, truthful, or loved as we could, we may feel anxious or depressed. We may feel guilty, angry, judged, fearful or lacking in purpose, in which case we will indeed feel unbalanced.

Using the colours of the Chakras help us connect and remember which is which. Our Root Chakra is our base and a good starting point. Going back to the base, I've found, is the essence of the Chakra system. That means if we don't feel balanced in a particular Chakra, dropping to the level below helps us implement ways of nurturing ourselves before moving forwards (or upwards).

1st Root Chakra – Muladhara

Survival
Grounded
Safe
Secure
Centred

Meaning: 'Root Support'
Situated: Base of the spine at the perineum
Words Associated: 'I am'
Balanced: Grounded, safe, security, trust, ability to relax and be still, centred, firm in your place in life. Happy to be alive.
Blocked: Instability, depressed, anxious, panic attacks, not feeling part of life, not feeling part of a community or group. Lower back problems, constipation, unexplained aches and pains
Overactive: Materialistic, Love for money and power. Driven by fear.
Colour: Red
Sense: Smell
Organs: Kidneys, Adrenal Gland (fight or flight response), Colon, Liver, Triple Heater (takes care of our immune system), Arterial Blood Flow
Crystals: Garnet, Ruby, Hematite, Black Tourmaline, Bloodstone, Onyx, Red Jasper
Aromatherapy Oils: Frankincense, Myrrh, Vetiver, Sandalwood, Spikenard

Our first Chakra is located at the base of our spines at the perineum. 'Moola' is the Sanskrit word meaning 'root' and could be acknowledged as our 'home', as this is where we feel safe, secure and assured. It's believed to be fundamental and lays the foundation in our lives as the base for the other six Chakras above it. Associated with the colour red, our Chakras above will begin to open and balance once this Chakra is awakened.

Water your roots so that your soul can blossom.

Our root Chakra supports our fundamental task of survival. It is here in the root Chakra that we aim to postpone death by eating, drinking, and breathing. Secondly, we look for security, shelter, and a home. Think of this Chakra as the foundations of a house or the roots of a tree, create good foundations and we then have a sturdy place to live. However, we may become fearful and afraid that we may not have *enough* to eat or *enough* to drink and it can spread into other areas of life; believing we don't have *enough* belongings or possessions or anything else we deem important, and this is where we can tip the balance. We can live in fear believing we need more and more 'stuff' to which we begin to associate ourselves with. Having done that, we enter 'The rat race' and subsequent stress via our thoughts and emotions that come with it. When balanced we feel grounded, committed, independent, and calm along with a strong sense of belonging, we feel at ease, eating, sleeping and procreating.

When we sit on our mats, we 'sit' on our root Chakra between the scrotum and anus in a man and as a diamond shape (forming a triangle between the pubic bone, coccyx, and inner thighs) in a woman. As we awaken our base Chakra, our body stimulates the thousands of energy channels which intertwine along our spine and endeavour to lift our energy upwards.

'Ground into your feet using your Mula Bandha, that area between your genitals and your anus'. Some yogis want to fall over with laughter when I mention sensitive body parts.
So funny, you've got to laugh!

If we're out of balance in this Chakra, we risk feeling anxious, worried, frustrated and even aggressive. We may get angry one moment and want to run away the next, having triggered our 'fight or flight' response. Having a family, network of people and/or a sense of community helps us find the security and belonging we seek. If we lost our homes, family, friends, or support network we would be out of balance in this Chakra resulting in a compromised platform for the flow of Prana or Chi above.

One of the most effective ways of reconnecting with a feeling of security and belonging is to understand who we are. As we are in fact, 'our own home'. Muladhara is associated with the words 'I am' and, our own 'I-am-ness'. This gives us the opportunity to challenge the labels and identifications we put upon ourselves. First though, let's look at how we view ourselves and understand how that can be helpful and work to our advantage.

'I am' a wife
'I am' a mother
'I am' a daughter
'I am' a sister
'I am' a friend
'I am' a yoga teacher
'I am' a coach
'I am' a hairdresser
'I am' someone who cares for others
'I am' an outdoor person who loves nature, animals, and trees
'I am' someone who loves sheds and quirky spaces
'I am' a wildly independent woman
'I am' ... many more things

Our Bliss List can also give us insight into our identity. Have a go at the above. Understanding who we are brings a fresh sense of comfort and brings us 'home'.

Here's an example:

'I am a mother'. What does that mean to me? Unconditional love, compassion, friendship, nurturing, laughter, and affection to name a few. With that, I aim to spend quality time with my children along with our family as a whole. It's important to me that my children feel loved and cherished. It's important they feel supported, and they know they have parents that love them alongside wanting them to establish their own lives, having the ability to 'fly', when or as often as they wish. Just writing these sentences re-engages my feelings around my love for my children and in turn what security, home and belonging looks and feels like to me. It could be as simple as picking up the phone and having a conversation. It could be making their own *(secret recipe)* get-well soup, it might be to offer my help around something they're interested in, or it might be simply to listen, to give them my absolute and full attention. The powerful thing here is, that it's *me* who will gain the positive grounding, belonging and secure feelings from this. It's *me* who will enjoy feeling more at home by simply becoming mindful of my own identity as a mother.

Being aware of what we stand for, helps us re-engage with who we are and what is meaningful to us. I aim to be a loving and caring wife, as a daughter I tend to my parent's grave, I've quite strangely taken responsibility for painting the shed in our village church yard purely through my identity as *a shed lover*. All actions add to my base, my home, and my feelings of security through purpose. You may want to identify the feelings of what home and stability means for you and how you bring it into reality.

Have a go:

I am a _____

I am a _____

I am a _____

You may feel a desire to do something around one of the above.

Yoga poses connected to Muladhara Chakra are those where our feet or body, is firmly planted on the ground:
- Tadasana or (Mountain Pose)
- Virabhadrasana (Warrior One and Two)
- Uttanasana (Standing forward Fold)
- Setu Bandhasana (Bridge Pose)
- Salabhasana (Locust Pose)
- Putting our legs up a wall (Viparita Karani Pose)

Standing postures require us to pull in our Mula Bandha, the first of the three Bandhas being the yogic energy centre at our perineum. By engaging this Bandha and drilling down we find ourselves even more connected with the earth beneath us. Lift and lower your toes in standing postures and notice how you feel.

The crystals associated with Muladhara can be placed on the body in Shavasana. Alternatively, we could put one of the red coloured stones by our bed at night or carry one in our purse or wallet to remind us of home and what home means to us.

When we feel balanced at our base Chakra, we feel committed, calm, stable and secure. Physically we feel strong, energetic, and powerful. We become solid in our foundation. If we feel afraid, coming back to our roots in Muladhara helps.

'The biggest mistake you can make in life is to continually be afraid you will make one.'
- Elbert Hubbard; Writer, Publisher, Artist

Affirmations for the Root Chakra include:
- 'I am safe'
- 'I enjoy good health'
- 'I am connected to my body'
- 'I am comfortable in my body'
- 'I am enough'
- 'I am a courageous warrior'
- 'I am emotionally grounded'
- 'I am my own bodyguard'

2nd Sacral Chakra – Svadhisthana

Creativity
Sexuality
Friendliness
Intimacy

Meaning: 'One's own place'
Situated: Womb, genitals, sacrum.
Words Associated: 'I feel'
Balanced: Emotional intelligence, joy, pleasure, passion, sexuality, creativity, healthy libido, optimism, freedom, friendly, open.
Blocked: Low libido, fear of intimacy, little to no creativity, isolated, lonely, unable to express emotions.
Lower back pain, sciatica, arthritis, hip issues, anaemia, overactive, overwhelm, mood swings, dissatisfaction
Overactive: Over emotional, hedonistic, sex addict, over passionate
Colour: Orange
Sense: Taste
Organs: Kidneys, urinary bladder, small intestine, liver, triple heater (Takes care of our immune system), reproductive gland
Crystals: Citrine, Moonstone, Amber, Calcite, Coral, Tiger's Eye
Aromatherapy Oils: Ylang Ylang, Rose, Sweet Orange, Tangerine

A balanced Svadhisthana Chakra increases feelings of optimism and wellbeing. Situated at the lower abdomen, Svadhisthana is associated with the colour orange and relates to the womb, hips, genitals (in both men and women) and sacrum. Often referred to as 'The Sexy Chakra'.

Svadhisthana is the centre for emotions and pleasure and is responsible for our relationships as well as our drive and desire to find love and intimacy. If someone is said to have genuine warmth and friendliness, they are said to have a healthy Sacral Chakra. Someone who respects their own body, has the ability to let go of unhealthy emotions and is happy to explore boundaries in a playful way. Balance in this Chakra gives us feelings of creativity, compassion, emotional stability and zest for life, as well as a great sense of fun and humour.

Svadhisthana lies in the sacrum area. Low back pain, sciatica, urinary problems and hormonal issues are associated with an imbalance in this Chakra as well as too high or too low libido. If we're too trusting of others, emotionally sensitive or have an obsessive unhealthy attachment, we may want to balance this Chakra. Being unable to express our emotions and desires is also attached to an imbalance in our Sacral Chakra.

Holding onto emotions can result in feelings of guilt and shame, fear of change, as well as feeling lethargic and heavy. Stress, emotional upset or conflict, also lies in the hands of this Chakra which ties in with menstrual pains and the changing emotions we experience towards and during the menopause.

Water is believed to balance the second Chakra as is drinking it and being around it. Sitting by a river, the sea, a pond or a lake. Sitting cross legged heightens this even more as we sit on our Root Chakra, balancing the two.

The moon, dancing alone like no-one is watching, walking in nature and sitting by water especially the sea, are all associated with Svadhisthana Chakra.

Carrying or placing the orange-coloured crystals; Citrine, Moonstone, Amber, Calcite, Coral or Tiger's Eye below your navel is said to help balance this Chakra.

Postures that balance our Sacral Chakra are all poses that open and stretch the groin and hips, including:
- Prasarita Padottanasana (standing wide-legged forward fold)
- Utkata Konasana (Goddess Pose)
- Malasana or Cobblers Pose (Yoga Squat)
- Supta Baddha Konasana (Reclined Bound Angle Pose)

- Upavistha Konasana or Dragonfly (seated wide-legged forward bend)
- Bhekasana (Frog Pose)
- Baddha Konasana or Butterfly (Bound Angle Pose)
- Skandasana (Deep lunge Pose)

As it's believed we hold emotions in our hips, letting go during many of these postures, especially in a Yin class, brings huge psychological benefits. Imagine our emotions floating towards us like clouds then drifting away without having to act on them, overthink them or hold them any longer. Yogis sometimes tell me they get the urge to laugh or cry in a class. Either is welcomed and often described as the chakras, especially svadhisthana balancing.

I believe when my back was at its worst, it was because I was emotionally upset. Ironically, I didn't get out in nature enough, I drank too much coffee instead of water and along with my daughter, sat for too many hours in hospitals. I remember one very traumatic time sitting outside a doctor's office. Dean drew a simple picture of our beach hut on a piece of paper and handed it to me. It made me pine. Our gorgeous blue beach hut (bought for just £100 twenty-two years ago) was sat by the sea waiting for us and it would only be a matter of time before we could enjoy the beach, the waves, the sea and the sand. We sold our hut some six years later and I missed the feeling that our little wooden seaside shed gave us.

Eighteen months ago, I found a dining chair in a ditch. I dragged it out, inspected it and instead of bringing it home and taking it to a tip, I carried it for another quarter of a mile and placed it beside a hedge in an un-farmed field. One with a nice view. I regained the feeling our seaside hut gave me, as the chair sat in the same place day in, day out, and became a destination point for those who discovered it. If anyone asked where it was, I told them they'd need to find it themselves. It stood unassuming for nearly two years amongst the sounds of nature. One day I was surprised and disappointed to see it had disappeared. It wasn't my chair and not my land and a reminder that nothing lasts forever, but I was thankful that it made me smile and connected me to a beautiful space in nature.

Svadhisthana is the centre for emotions. Here's what emotionally balanced looks like:

- You feel understood by those you love
- You feel safe to share your feelings and insecurities
- You enjoy autonomy and freedom
- You feel open and 'go with the flow'
- You feel accepted (foibles and all)
- You encourage and receive encouragement
- You feel safe to show your shadow (remember Madge!)
- You're happy being perfectly imperfect
- You're comfortable sharing your dreams
- You feel at ease with silence and quiet
- You value non-sexual contact
- You share a deep respect for yourself and others
- You feel safe to share your emotions
- You frequently let go of what was

Looking at this list and then back at our past, we have a deeper understanding why those relationships or friendships didn't flourish after all.

Svadhisthana is possibly my favourite Chakra because it's associated with being open, friendly, creative and a little wild. When we stretch the groin and hips it helps us feel lighter, takes the pressure off our lower backs and lifts our spirits.

Svadhisthana is our place of passion. Passion resonates with the word 'I' as things we are passionate about speak of the self. Passions could be identified as interests and absorptions, even selfishness by others. They're personal and about *self, me,* or *I,* to possibly include uncontrollable emotion. We definitely need to know ourselves before we can share ourselves authentically with the world. I'm passionate about yoga and I'm passionate about sheds. Thing is, I'd be the only one benefiting from them, which is absolutely fine and a choice but also in my opinion, a bit of a shame. Why? Because when our time ends in this world, so will our passions.

If we become too passionate about anything in life, a hobby, career, or relationship, we may risk consuming ourselves into that one encompassing desire, possibly leading to deterioration in other areas of life. Family, friendships, and even our own health and wellbeing can easily become compromised creating an imbalance in this Chakra and our life. Embracing and being proud of our passions is important but also being aware of keeping them healthy is essential to our happiness.

Purpose on the other hand could be identified as something bigger, shared, and inclusive. Something that creates reason, value, and usefulness. Through purpose our goals are based on a bigger picture and not just our own needs and wants, or our expectations of ourselves, driven by our egos. Turning a passion into a purpose is a great way of giving us direction and intention, as well as helping us detach ourselves from our ego. Having a purpose doesn't need to have anything to do with whether we get paid, or how much money we make or don't make. It's about sharing what we have for the benefit of ourselves *and* others. It's a great way to create new friendships and build connections as well as a community all attributing to a sense of belonging in the world.

By creating a purpose from a passion we've brought together a community of likeminded people affectionately named 'Yoga Sheddies', having different interests to include our pets, running, reading, gardening, litter picking, Morris dancing, baking, hiking, SUP boarding and much more. I encourage anyone to bring their passions to the table to share.

*'If you can't figure out your purpose,
figure out your passion.
For your passion will lead you
right into your purpose.'*

- Bishop T.D. Jakes

Svadhisthana relates to being open and friendly but what if we're too open or too friendly? Does that mean this Chakra is out of balance? Yes.

Before I left the UK, Dean told me not to go off with strangers. I was forty-seven and on the last two days of my course in San Diego. I, along with the last few attendees, were at a loose end with no transport. A man from Texas, whose name I've forgotten (however, during a conversation he said his daughter's name was Wren, which led me to believe he was hip/cool), had planned to go to the beach and as I had no car and no transport, I asked if I could join him. That evening my Texan roommate took me to one side and suggested I make myself and my intentions very clear to this man. 'Why?' I asked.

'Because he thinks you want a sexual relationship with him.'

'Really? I just want to go to the beach!' So, at breakfast I made it very clear that I'm happily married with two children and thought I might take advantage of his company, his car, and the fact that he was going to the beach. An hour later, I was sat in the passenger seat being driven down the highway. I'm well-travelled and have met many people, but at that moment I realised I was with someone I didn't know, in a rented car that was traveling too fast, in a country I'm not entirely familiar with and heading for a destination that could have been anywhere! It was at that point that I realised I'd put myself in a bad situation. This, at the age of forty-seven, is a good example of my Svadhisthana Chakra and my boundaries being a little over balanced. The beach wasn't as nice as I imagined it to be although Michael (Ah, that was his name), said he thought it was idyllic whilst trying to hold my hand. He suggested we make love on the sand; I politely said I wasn't interested, thank you, instead I asked if he'd heard of North Norfolk, and took myself for a paddle.

If we feel emotional, stuck, or irritable due to a relationship problem and find ourselves feeling guilty, obsessed, or blaming, it helps to bring our attention back to Muladhara Chakra and work on grounding ourselves and our environment. Stepping back and doing the work, helps us to move forwards.

Edith Eger is a Holocaust survivor and author of *The Gift. She* believes we are all hungry for attention, affection, and approval. 'We are hungry for the freedom to embrace life and to know and be ourselves, we become victims not because of what happens to us but when we choose to hold onto our victimisation. That we hold a victim's mind - a way of thinking and being that is rigid, blaming, pessimistic, stuck in the past, unforgiving, punitive and without healthy limits or boundaries. We become our own jailors when we choose the confines of the victims mind'.

Attention, affection, and *approval* sit well alongside this Chakra and are incredibly useful when understanding relationships with others and ourselves. Through personal experience and supporting others, I've become aware of how important all three contribute towards our feelings of wholeness.

How do we feel if we're not given attention?
How do we feel if we are starved of affection?
How do we feel if we are not given approval or acceptance?

How do others feel if we give *them* insufficient attention, affection, or approval?

To enable us to enjoy healthy relationships the above must apply both ways, alongside how we treat ourselves. Without benefiting from attention, affection, and approval, we risk having an unbalanced second Chakra.

Svadhisthana applies to these questions:
- What helps you feel free?
- What is creativity to you?
- What brings you pleasure?
- How do you allow yourself to feel pleasure?
- Who brings out the best in you?

- Are you stuck in a Drama Triangle?
- How easy is it for you to say no?
- What are you emotionally carrying?
- What do you need to lovingly walk away from?

Affirmations for Svadhisthana can include:
- 'I feel pleasures in life'
- 'I experience healthy relationships'
- 'I feel emotionally secure'
- 'I release my emotions'
- 'I celebrate my sexuality'
- 'I enjoy free flow of movement'
- 'My body is open'
- 'My sexuality is sacred'

'I think it's beautiful the way you sparkle when you
talk about the things you love.'
- Atticus

We balance our Svadhisthana Chakra by enjoying pleasure in life, adding creativity, delighting in healthy relationships, and embarking in pastimes that give us a feeling of freedom and maybe a little wildness.

Life goal.
Wanting to dance around a campfire naked.
Join me!

3rd Solar Plexus Chakra – Manipura

Will Power
Confidence
Self Esteem
Drive

Meaning: 'Brilliant or Lustrous Gem'
Situated: Above the navel, behind the stomach
Words Associated: 'I do'
Balanced: Happy, high self-esteem, confidence, productivity, motivation, self-discipline, drive, healthy self-image, feeling in control, assertive, healthy boundaries.
Blocked: doubt, mistrust, low self-esteem, submissive, inferiority complex, feeling like you can't get ahead, lazy. Eating disorders, irritable bowel syndrome, ulcers.
Overactive: Power hungry, perfectionist, domineering.
Colour: Yellow
Sense: Sight
Organs: Stomach, Spleen, Liver, Gallbladder, Large Intestine, Small Intestine
Crystals: Amber, Agate, Orange Calcite, Citrine, Topaz, Tiger's Eye
Aromatherapy Oils: Myrrh, Ylang Ylang, Lemongrass, Helichrysum, Lavender

When our Solar Plexus Chakra is balanced, we feel motivated and inspired. We feel confident, decisive, and productive, we become reliable, self-disciplined, and accepting of change. We have strong boundaries and enjoy high self-esteem. Physically, we have good digestion, healthy metabolism, and a strong diaphragm. This Chakra is associated with our liver which is said to be 'The energy of our personality'. Our liver is responsible for ridding our body of UFO's known as unidentified food objects to include medications, toxins, additives, alcohol, and hormones. The liver is said to help digest what we consume along with the digestion of our emotions.

We often complain of a stomach-ache when we feel emotional or anxious.

If this Chakra is imbalanced our self-esteem drops, we may feel depressed, insecure, lose our sense of self or fear rejection. We may use aggression as a means of feeling better or we may find ourselves judging others and ourselves, as well as wanting everything in our world to be perfect.

Manipura is our Chakra for healthy boundaries. Whilst I was on that crazy course in San Diego, I noticed that a lot of women would politely say 'Excuse me, I need to go outside to get some fresh air' or 'Excuse me, I need to go back to my room for some time alone before we start studying again'. I found it rather interesting because it wasn't something I feel many women in the UK say or do. Most women I know, including myself, will stay until the last woman is standing (or chatting). We tend not to deal with our own needs or requirements, in favour of the group or the other person, refraining from wanting to say no, appear selfish, or self-absorbed. It's challenging to find the balance between honouring our own needs whilst not thinking ourselves more important than others. Many of the American women I met, surprised me with their acceptance and confidence around their personal boundaries, at the same time I caught myself thinking, 'My life needs a bit more of this'.

Self-love; being in love with every part of yourself. Taking care of your own needs and not sacrificing your wellbeing to please others. Not settling for less than you deserve.

Our home is a good reflection of our personal boundaries. Those who have been stolen from or burgled, often want to move house in the name of feeling disrespected. Placing your (wine) glass for instance, too near someone during a conversation over dinner will give you a visual demonstration of personal boundaries as they move your glass away. Try it, it'll make you smile; an effective way of seeing how we hold our boundaries unconsciously.

But personal boundaries aren't always easy to create or maintain; most of us have experienced people who drain us physically and emotionally leaving us feeling exhausted, yet we go back for more because we're either unaware of the effect it has on us or because we're afraid to break free.

A friend of mine shared with me that his home help and cleaner steals food and items from his cupboards each time she works at his home. He explained to me that he's afraid to mention anything to her in fear that he damages their friendship. I sensitively shared my thoughts, suggesting she's already damaging their friendship simply by stealing from him. I suggested he consider his boundaries; clarifying what is acceptable to him and what is not. After all, what belongs to him is for him to give, and not for her to take. It's up to us to take responsibility for our own boundaries, our time and who and what, shares our energy. Strong personal boundaries sit alongside high self-esteem; when we nurture self-love, we improve our self-esteem. When we improve our self-esteem, we are less likely to allow others to overstep our boundaries. This could be a good metaphor for our own situations where there are no, or weak boundaries.

Refrain from allowing others to step on your mats.
It's your mat and your space.
Let our mat teach us about boundaries.

Mystery

'Be a mystery', my Mum said,
'A mystery? ... Bit old fashioned!'

Looking back,
I think she meant,
Look after your boundaries.

You can 'just say no', yoga girl
to anything.
You don't have to explain,
not 'no because...'
Just No
or maybe - enough!

I thought a boundary
was a fence,
I understand.
a dividing line,
a separation,

Narrow as a stream,
Wide as an ocean,
We choose.

A woman who understands healthy boundaries,
Is a strong woman - indeed.

No - I can't.
No - I'm busy.
No - but thanks anyway.
Or, just Nope!

My Mum knew that,
I always thought,
She was a mystery.

- Manda

We can say 'no'. We don't have to give an explanation. We don't have to say 'no, because'. We don't have to share how we feel, we can just say 'No' or 'Nope' or 'Enough'.

Sometimes we struggle with our boundaries leaving us feeling manipulated in a destructive cycle that we find hard to escape from. I've used a particular 'tool', time and time again when coaching others and for that reason I'd like to share it with you. First identified by Stephen Karpman in 1961 'The Drama Triangle' helps us firstly recognise we're in the cycle and secondly helps us to refuse to play it.

The triangle has three points; the persecutor, the victim and the rescuer and is usually played out between two people. One person sits at any point of the triangle and the other unconsciously steps into one of the three points as a reaction. The two involved move around the triangle in any order and this is how we become 'stuck'.

Here's an example:
*Becky gets angry with Peter because Peter was three hours late to work with no explanation. Becky uses language and sarcasm that isn't appropriate. She has chosen to be **the persecutor** and sits on one of the points of the triangle. She feels angry and irritated.*

*Peter unconsciously reacts and becomes **the victim,** standing at one of the other points of the triangle. He feels scolded and upset. In doing so, he refuses to speak to her or even make eye contact during a business meeting the following day.*

*Becky decides his behaviour during the meeting is not acceptable, she too unconsciously goes into the same place as **the victim** sharing her feelings with shared colleagues. She feels isolated and ignored.*

*Peter notices that he's being spoken about behind his back, which he doesn't like. He angrily steps into **the persecutor** role and calls her using a threatening voice alongside some* *personal insults. Becky also steps **from victim into persecutor** and shouts back. Both now feel stressed and fractious.*

*The next day Peter decides to stop off on his way to work and buys two coffees in what he believes to be a peace offering. He has now moved into **the rescuer** position. Becky, instead of accepting his offer of the coffee, continues as **the persecutor** and aggressively insinuates that he's trying to manipulate her.*

Isn't it wearing? Maybe you can relate? What do we do to stop this from happening? How do we prevent the movement from one point to another point of the triangle?

Answer: we simply don't play the game and refuse to go to any point. If we want to understand a little more, we need to understand each orientation. Understand that if we feel **victimised**, we must recognise the effect this is having on us. Do we want to feel bullied, belittled, or persecuted? We can identify this whilst on our mats, during pauses and in meditation. Understand the **persecutor** orientation, do we really want angry negative feelings festering in our mind and body? We can use our yoga practice, especially breath work to calm and soften our minds and create clarity. Understand the **rescuer** orientation, do we feel good about giving our attention, affection, or love to someone who is hurting us? Do we feel good trying to manipulate a situation? Yoga can help us consider our actions and decisions, maintain, or build self-love.

Realise that when two people are following the same game there are no winners, there is only room for hurt, stress, tension, and unhappiness.

What if you're in the triangle with another but, for whatever reason, you don't want to get out of it? It then becomes a choice. Our actions have consequences and it's up to us to take personal responsibility. NLP (or Neuro linguistic programming) has a principle which suggests that everything we do has a positive intent. If we don't want to leave the triangle, we could ask ourselves what the positive intent of staying in it is? Will feeling like a victim help us wallow in our own self-pity? Will we feel unburdened if we get angry as the persecutor? Will we have the perfect situation to demonstrate our goodwill in the rescuer position? What is the short-term positive intent and the heavy cost to ourselves over time?

Meditation will help us feel peace within ourselves, breathing deeply will bring us into the moment allowing us time to think and not react. A Yin practice will help us nurture and love ourselves. A Yang practice helps us create a strong body. Inversions will help us see the other person's point of view and hip openers will help us let go.

If we find ourselves in the drama triangle or have recognised that we've been in it for a while, practising ways of becoming the creator of our own outcomes will help. The situation might not change instantly because it may be a new way of thinking and behaving. Allowing ourselves time for change will be the kindest thing we can do, rather than continue to play a game with unrelenting negative consequences.

Going to our mats can massively help us escape the triangle. I call my mat a retreat for a reason.

You've stared at your Bliss List, you've identified your passions and possibly, a purpose. You can literally see what you want more of in life, be it trees, sheds, baking cakes, balancing on a board, or walking up mountains. Maybe like me, you've identified something that feels good. It might not be earth-shattering, and it may not be a job or a career change, it could be something you just want to do more of and maybe share with others.

We become what we repeatedly do.

Manipura Chakra is also associated with confidence and self-esteem. Lack of confidence is debilitating and is one of the obstacles that prevents us achieving what we want, possibly leaving us feeling as though we'd lost an opportunity or let ourselves down.

If we're aiming to achieve something we have a personal affection or connection to, our confidence is naturally greater, so we're more likely to achieve it.

Doubt, mistrust, low self-esteem, and laziness can manifest if Manipura Chakra is out of balance. I love this quote about yoga by Pattabhi Jois:

Anyone can practice.
Young man can practice.
Old man can practice.
Very old man can practice.
Man who is sick, he can practice.
Man who doesn't have strength can practice.
Except lazy people;
lazy people can't practice Ashtanga yoga.

Overconfidence is also an imbalance in this Chakra which encourages us to rely on our ego, leading us towards dominance, aggression, the need for perfection and judgement towards ourselves or others, in order to support and carry us forward.

We're awake for sixteen to eighteen hours a day, and many of us privately spend too much time viewing others in a judgmental or competitive way. We've all done it! When we point a finger at another, we're often unaware that we have three fingers pointing back at ourselves. We can help balance this Chakra by seeing in ourselves what we see in others, if we can see something negative in others, possibly we can identify the same behaviour in ourselves, purely because we can relate to it.

Yeah, ouch!

Many Life Coaches use what's called a Behavioural Drivers Test to help those they're supporting learn more about themselves, what influences them and in turn, how they behave or react. Our behavioural drivers are our values which are taught to us by others from a young age. They can help us and hinder us. They certainly play a part in finger pointing!

There are five behavioural drivers.

Please Others - Aiming to please. Being agreeable
Be Quick - Feeling the need to do it now. Efficiency
Be Perfect - Aiming to be flawless. Exemplary
Be Strong - Not crying, not cracking. Carrying too much
Try Harder - Not reaching desired outcomes. Endeavouring

I have found these very interesting and personally beneficial. I was raised by two busy and capable parents. They taught me unconsciously to *'Be quick'* and *'Be strong'*. This has resulted in me being quick or efficient and a 'go to' person, if you want to get a job done. I was also unconsciously taught to 'be strong', I was taught to cope whatever the outcome. This has been a good thing enabling me to cope for years with our daughter's eye condition and my own back issues, but in other ways it has stopped me showing vulnerability, as well as not allowing myself to cry, be seen to cry or even ask for help. Knowing my drivers has made me aware, and in turn I now aim to slow down, take my time, as well as ask for help; and even allow myself to be vulnerable, which to date has only been with a few close people.

We can relate to all the drivers, but there is a high probability that one or two will be more relatable. For instance, if you have a high *'Please others'* behavioural driver, you might spend much of your time invested in others aiming to be liked or accepted. A *'Be quick'* driver might make you super-efficient and able to pack lots into life but may leave you feeling tired or exhausted. If you have a high *'Be perfect'* driver, you may find that you seek perfection in one or several ways, thinking you're not good enough. Being constantly *'Strong'* may result in you feeling lonely and unable to express your emotions. Lastly if you resonate with a *'try harder'* behavioural driver, you might identify that you're putting immense amounts of pressure on yourself and never being satisfied. Looking at the list above, may enable you to identify one or two with ease.

Paying attention to our actions and emotions is helpful. Our drivers can help us identify where these frustrations come from, and can explain why some behaviours in others go straight over our heads, and why some people's behaviour gets on our nerves.

We cannot fix others, but we can fix ourselves. Zig Ziglar calls it 'stinking thinking'. It's important for our self-esteem that we work on our own bullshit before we waste our time identifying others.

Sometimes I feel emotionally low. I feel mentally exhausted because I've tried to pack too much into my day, or I feel overwhelmed because I've been strong for others and forgotten myself. Sometimes I don't like aspects of myself making unfair comparisons and judging myself unkindly. Those kinds of days are when my yoga practice turns my psyche around. I use the words associated with this Chakra 'I do' and I do literally, go to my mat. Within an hour I can go from feeling overwhelmed with 'stinking thinking', to feeling much calmer and content. I constantly thank all aspects of yoga for helping me to disentangle my mind.

We're allowed bad days. We don't have to feel happy all the time. We're human. We're designed to rise and fall just like the waves.

Manipura being associated with motivation, goes hand in hand with goal setting. As an accredited coach, I supported others for five years. It was very enjoyable but as time passed, I became frustrated. I needed to spend my time being more physical and less time sitting. It drained my energy, hurt my lower back, and took me away from who I am. It wasn't the right way for me even though at the time, I hadn't identified it was movement and physicality I needed. It's quite powerful when we identify small but significant facts about ourselves.

Coaching is based on goal setting, a goal in this context is something we want to achieve, and not something we kick a football into. It's something we want to *Be, Do* or *Have* that we don't already have or experience. Most goals are centred around work/careers, relationships or health and fitness.

I want to explain here how the feeling of happiness fits into goal setting, and how this changed my thoughts around traditional coaching and led me towards the physicality of yoga which connects to the word *movement* on my bliss list.

Imagine you want to achieve something. Now imagine yourself standing on the left-hand side of a piece of paper, which could be this book, and imagine your goal (whatever it is, that you want to *be, do,* or *have*) on the right-hand side of this book. There's a gap between where you are and where you want to be. Imagine a 'dip' in the middle. This 'dip' is the reason why most people don't get to the right-hand side and is relied upon by those who want to be *successful*.

In the modern Western world, we are taught to want to get to the other side. The Eastern world is more centred on the power of now.

Underneath our goal or goals sit our values. Our values are held unconsciously and help us to achieve what we want. It's one of the aims of a coach to identify those unconscious values and use them to help, support and motivate the client to reach that goal.

In my case, I was a coach who was spending time sitting on a chair, listening to others sometimes for hours. I enjoyed the work but too much sitting left me feeling stagnant, stiff and miserable. I needed to move. I'll use the goal of wanting 'movement' as a simple example. I'm on the left-hand side and my goal is on the right-hand side. There is a dip in the middle. I want to get from the left to the right.

To find the value(s), I need to ask what I want from *movement.*
What will *movement* bring me? *A feeling of freedom.*
What else? *Better blood flow.*
What else? *Energy.*
What else? *The ability to be more expressive and creative.*

What does a feeling of *freedom, better blood flow, energy, expression, and creativity* bring me a feeling of?

Happiness.

The thing is our unconscious values always boil down to two words: happiness and/or contentment. Asking may encourage a list of words but the end word or value, will always end up with the word (and feeling) of happiness.

This also implies that many of us are standing on the left-hand side of the paper, staring at what we want, which sits on the right-hand side of the paper alongside our feelings of happiness.

Therefore, there's a gap between where we are and happiness. We start to believe that ...

We won't be happy until we get that job.
We won't be happy until we get that pay rise
We won't be happy until we go on holiday
We won't be happy until we retire
We won't be happy until we can do 'a crow pose'

It's here we can get stuck, feeling miserable, frustrated and even angry.

What could have been in my dip? In this context, my ego. Wanting to *appear* professional as a coach, wanting to do what I believed to be 'right', not being honest with myself and my own personal needs. Being part of the 'rat-race'.

There is no doubt that goals push us forwards, however, putting ourselves in a position of chronic stress being stuck in the 'The Dip' in our quest for happiness, is a terrible waste of precious time. Happiness is achievable today once we remove our ego and become real and honest with ourselves and our lives. Many of us are needlessly spending our time in limbo, frustrated, discontented and living in fear of not having or being enough.

Our yoga practice helps us put the ego to one side
It's like a breath of fresh air

Once this realisation of fear and misplaced happiness came to me, it changed the way I thought about traditional coaching and changed the way I think about life. I circled 'happiness' underneath my goals and drew a big fat line from the right-hand side of the paper back to the left. It felt good. Why? Because I'd brought my own personal feeling of happiness into today where it belongs.

Happiness is now, not next week, next month or next year.
We need to understand that. When we go to our mats, we're
there in the moment doing what we can – today.

'When I was five years old,
My mother always told me that,
Happiness was the key to life.

When I went to school,
They asked me what I wanted to be,
When I grew up.

I wrote down 'Happy'

They told me that I didn't
Understand the assignment,
And I told them that
They didn't understand life'

John Lennon

This revelation and feeling was immense. It completely made sense to me to the point where it didn't fit the ideology of the company I was being employed by. I sat with the Director one afternoon and put myself out of work based on this theory. Unless the underlying value of happiness could be brought into the here and now, my clients would continue to experience and endure negative stress found in 'The Dip', because they either weren't the right person for the position, or weren't invested in the goals that were designated to them. My integrity, and in turn respect, got full marks but my bank balance took the knock.

Ouch! Totally worth it!

Bringing happiness to the here and now endorses who we are, which is more powerful than we might initially believe. Too many people suffer from unnecessary stress, because they're either chasing a feeling of happiness, or aiming to achieve something that they're not invested in.

Yoga teaches us to be real and honest with ourselves

Our Bliss List can help identify what means most to us, which is in alignment with who we are and not who we *think* we are, or worse, who others want us to be. We're already invested.

From my Bliss List I saw and understood that I wanted and needed *movement* in my life. The word 'movement' boiled down to 'happiness' but also connected to other words I'd written on my list. Movement might not mean anything to you but the ability to literally move means a lot to me. It means freedom, blood circulation and energy, all leading to me feeling happier. Instead of wondering what my goal was or struggling to realise what my goal might be, I just stared at my list until the answer came, and when it did, it was so obvious. Whatever I do, I need to move!

From your list you have already identified passions and possibly a purpose. You have the foundation for change if that's what you want. Knowing what's good, and right for you is a positive and energetic place to be or start, and best of all, you're far more likely to glide over 'The Dip' because you're choosing something that is already part of you. You're choosing from a solid and trusted base. Goals simply become easier to attain.

If we do nothing, nothing will happen. If we want something we need to get out of our comfort zone and pass the 'Oh sh*t point'. Taking the attitude 'I'll take a leap and trust my wings will appear' can work, however sometimes it's good to sleep at night, creep into our future and make a plan.

We have two different ways of achieving what we want, depending on the size and time frame of our goal.

1. 'Feel the fear and do it anyway' - throw yourself into the situation which can feel liberating and most effective as you're already invested and interested.
2. Create achievable bite sized goals, break them down into stages and make a step-by-step plan.

Actions have consequences and not everything works, or works the first time. We need to be prepared to give things a go, and we need to be prepared to fail, more than once if necessary.

On our mat, we may want to try a headstand for instance. We could go all-in but crash. For some it'll work first time, for most of us, it'll be more effective to break it down and work our way towards it.

Having a goal around something we feel invested in will make the journey a whole lot easier. Let's face it, there's nothing harder than trying to achieve something we don't really want, which includes what our ego, habits, expectations, bosses, or partners might want. This is where we must drill down and be completely honest with ourselves.

It's useful to embrace failure; through failure we receive feedback; from feedback we learn. Successful people accept failure as part of the process, and through that they build resilience. Psychologists define resilience as a process of adapting well in the face of adversity, we could call it bounce-back-ability.

'I bend so that I don't break.'

Some of us bounce back quicker or easier than others; during our practice there are days when our poses don't work, when we nose plant or fall against a wall trying something we're not yet strong enough for. However, if we continually commit to our practice, break things down and return to our mats, we notice that we create or increase our resilience. Not everything works on the mat and not everything works in life. Over time we learn to step away and come back stronger, we start to strengthen our mind-set, and not only become more adaptable to change but also thrive on the journey. All we need to do is keep going to our mats.

'A goal properly set is halfway reached.'
- Zig Ziglar

Want something? Write down what it is you want, you might notice you have several words on your List that already sit alongside, compliment or endorse what you want. In which case, you have a happy bundle!

1. Write down your goal, what is what you want.
2. Make sure it's achievable even if it's scary.
3. Write down a sentence as though you've already achieved it.
4. Ask yourself if you like the sound and feel of that.
5. Write down *why* you want this goal.
6. Put a date next to your goal when you want to achieve it. *If it doesn't have a date, it's just a dream.*
7. Write down what will happen when you've achieved it.
8. Write down what will happen if you *don't* achieve it.
9. Break down your journey, list the steps that need to happen and add a date to each step.
10. Ask yourself how committed you are to achieving your goal.

11. Based on the Bliss List; If you don't feel excited and committed you have the wrong goal. #justsaying.
12. Write down the smallest, tiniest step you could take right now.
13. Do that.
14. Do something every day to step closer to your goal.

Monica: 'Do you have a plan?'
Phoebe: 'I don't even have a pla.'

I've created a few travel goals over the years and experienced a few places alone (including Scotland, America, Greece, and Singapore) but I'll use my journey to India to become a yoga instructor as my goal and example. Planning felt easy and enjoyable simply because I was in alignment with what I wanted and not what my ego, my expectations of myself or others wanted for me.

I wrote down my goal of wanting to share yoga and teach, and then wrote down why I wanted to teach. The 'Why?' question is very important as it highlights all the benefits of achieving that goal and brings about the motivation to complete it. My answer to this question took up a whole page. This question will also help you identify if you're moving towards pleasure or moving away from pain.

I highly recommend that your goal moves you towards *pleasure,* as goals that take us away from pain are harder to maintain, as motivation reduces each time we get nearer to our goal.

'I want to practice yoga because I want to be flexible and strong'.
This is an example of a 'moving towards' goal.
'I want to start yoga because I'm stiff and I don't move well'.
This is an example of a 'moving away' goal.

'Moving away' goals can motivate us quickly because there's an element of pain attached to them, however, for long term motivation, check that your goals move 'towards' pleasure.

I knew the date I'd qualify so I wrote that down, then I wrote a list of everything I would need to happen between booking my training and starting my first class.

I thought about the steps, and I thought about the steps between the steps. I wrote a date next to everything I needed to achieve which made each intention very real. I even posted my goal and steps towards it on Facebook to demonstrate to others that creating goals does work. As I achieved each step, I ticked them off. Let me tell you, whatever the goal, ticking feels good!

Based on my Bliss List I felt happy.
Happy is relaxed and relaxed is easier.

This was the list I posted on Facebook on 18th January 2019:

1. Keep calm and pack - Right now
2. Go to India - Next Tuesday
3. Gain my qualification in yoga - End Feb 2019
4. Come home, cuddle husband, children, and dog
5. Change Facebook header and info - 28th Feb 2019
6. Book hall and pay deposit – 28th Feb 2019
7. Start advertising classes - 28th Feb 2019
8. Buy all yoga materials - 5th March 2019
9. Get more public liability insurance - 15th March 2019
10. Buy a room heater and PPL license - 15th March 2019
11. Look into hygiene course online - 20th March 2019
12. Book onto first aid course - 20th March 2019
13. Work on content of workshops - 20th March 2019
14. Order advertising boards - 1st April 2019
15. Order print work - 1st April 2019
16. Teach first Yoga class - 10th March 2019
17. Deliver first yoga workshop - May 2019

I knew I'd learn what I needed to, once I started the course, so I trusted in the process. Other women learning alongside me were surprised when I told them I'd already booked a hall. I was fully aware I wouldn't know all there is to know, I'm still fully aware, two and a half years later, that I still haven't learnt all there is to learn. Learning and curiosity continues. We can only trust that we are where we are, in any given time and be happy with that.

When we get out of our comfort zone, we can change our world. Many postures especially arm balances, take us out of our comfort zone and into our fear zone (Affectionately named 'Oh sh*t zone'). It's in those moments of fear during arm balances, where the magic happens, which helps us make those scary but important changes or new directions in life too.

Was I nervous? Yes.
Did I think I was a little crazy? Yes.
Did it stop me? No!
What was the worst thing that could happen?
I'd cancel the hall.

As humans, we feel fear, originally based on the fear of not having the security of water, food and shelter.
To grow and develop, we may need to de-value our emotional attachment to security.

Crystals such as Topaz, Sunstone, Amber, Agate, Orange Calcite, Tiger's Eye and Citrine are associated with the Solar Plexus Chakra. Placing these stones just above our naval in Shavasana or maybe carrying a small stone in our purse or wallet can remind us to assert ourselves, help us to be purposeful, self-disciplined, and cross 'The Dip' with ease, knowing that we've doing something that excites us, based on our psyche and not what our parents wanted us to do, our partner want us to do, society, or our ego.

When we have a goal, whatever our goal, asking why we want it, creates clarity. Asking others why they are doing or attempting something can sound too questioning, invasive, or challenging, however asking ourselves is helpful. Asking *why* in any area of life brings focus and clarity like shining a light through a torch.

Asking yourself *why:*
Why do I want to **be** (whatever it is you want to be?)
Why do I want to **do** (whatever it is you want to do?)
Why do I want to **have** (whatever it is you want to have?)

You could ask *why* in general life to help create clarity:
Why do I want this?
Why am I doing this?
Why do I enjoy this?
Why am I in this job or career?
Why am I in this relationship?
Why am I accepting this?
Why am I listening to this?
Why am I thinking this?

> *The two words why and because, are triggers.*
> *They require a response.*
> *When we ask 'why', we respond with, 'because'*
> *Our response invites us to dig deep.*
> *The answers give us deeper understanding and clarity.*

Why do you practice yoga?

Knowing the answer helps endorse why we practice but also helps us continue if or when we lose our motivation.

Here are three reasons why I practice yoga.

1. I practice Yoga because: Yoga brings me feelings of support. I've been self-employed since I was nineteen, which is a long time working on my own. Yoga feels like a good friend that I can rely on. I can roll out my mat when it suits me. I always feel in a better, more relaxed, and supported place after spending time on my mat.

2. I practice yoga because: It gives me a way of being and living. I feel I have the potential to be a little wild or crazy, therefore I value a few boundaries and rules even though I detest boundaries and rules and I love being wild and crazy. I'm a Gemini which might explain this.

3. I practice yoga because: I like being on the floor. Possibly connected to that faux leather suite and feeling calmer sat on the carpet. The floor feels safe and positive. I feel good when I'm on the floor and great when I'm on my mat.

There's enough evidence here to endorse my personal practice. By asking *why* I practice, results in greater motivation to continue. You may want to write down three reasons for practising yoga *or anything else* you have on your mind right now.

Why do you do (xyz)?

I do (xyz) because ....

Postures to help balance Manipura Chakra tend to be asanas that either need core stability or that require bending or twisting. They encourage us to feel strong and stable and capable of reaching our dreams.

- Surya Namaskar (The Sun Salutations)
- Any twists
- Navasana (Boat Pose)
- Planking
- Virabhadrasana (Warrior One, Two and Three)
- Dhanurasana (Bow Pose)

Someone with a balanced Manipura Chakra:
- Enjoys high confidence and self-esteem
- Is motivated
- Has high energy levels
- Gives things a go
- Is purposeful and reliable
- Makes decisions
- Creates goals
- Enjoys transformation
- Is full of vitality
- Works on resilience
- Has healthy boundaries

Affirmations for the Manipura Chakra
- 'I create goals based on what makes *me* happy'
- 'I make my own decisions with confidence'
- 'I'm motivated to pursue my passions with purpose'
- 'I happily give things a go knowing they might not work'
- 'Failure is only feedback for next time'

Balance your Manipura chakra when you want to reach your goals, when you want to bring more energy, confidence, productivity, and motivation into your life, and remember, if you don't want to do something, you don't want to do it! We also show our confidence when we communicate that we *don't want to do* something.

Do it, Ditch it or Decide it's not for you. All are correct.

4ᵗʰ Heart Chakra – Anahata

Love
Compassion
Peace
Acceptance
Gratitude

Meaning: 'Un-stuck' or 'un-hurt'
Situated: Heart, behind the sternum
Words Associated: 'I love'
Balanced: Loving, compassionate, peaceful, empathetic, kind, connection, unconditional love, acceptance, forgiveness, gratitude, meaningful relationships.
Blocked: Bitter, hateful, lack of empathy, intolerant, trust issues, lack of connection, lonely, isolated, fear of rejection, unemotional appearance, cold distant, suffocating others with love, love for selfish reasons
Poor blood circulation, heart palpitations,
Overactive: Self-sacrificing, co-dependent, giving away too much, putting others before ourselves, not able to find independence.
Colour: Green, or pale pink
Sense: Touch
Organs: Heart, Lungs, Blood Circulation, Small Intestine, Heart Constrictor (protection of circulation of the arteries and veins)
Crystals: Emerald, Green Calcite, Jade, Green Tourmaline, Rose Quartz
Aromatherapy Oils: Geranium, Jasmine, Lavender, Mandarin, Neroli

Anahata is recognised by the colour green but sometimes pale pink; the only Chakra recognised with two colours. When balanced we are kind, loving and compassionate. Physically we are said to have a good immune system, which suggests love keeps us healthy.

When in doubt, love, love, love, as an unbalanced Heart Chakra can leave us feeling depressed and jealous alongside a lack of empathy. And because we're trying to protect our hearts, we may become hunched and rounded in order to guard ourselves against rejection. According to yogic belief, being hunched over and 'closed' can be a sign that we've given away too much of ourselves.

'Heart' or chest opening asanas, open and balance the fourth Chakra helping us confront our situations and feelings. Attention to this Chakra helps us build self-acceptance, hopefulness, compassion, and peace.

We could say that everyone has a price, that price isn't measured in money but in love, specifically self-love. When we love ourselves, we have a high value which means we're unlikely to abuse ourselves or let anyone else abuse us. If we like ourselves and the way we are, our value continues to remain high but if we 'fall out' with ourselves or dislike ourselves, our value drops.

'Sometimes I worry you'll all realise I'm ordinary' said the boy. 'Love doesn't need you to be extraordinary.' said the Mole. - Charlie Mackesy

Our ego is there to protect us, so if we believe our value has dropped, we may create a persona which will work until we become exhausted, purely because we can't consistently be who we are not. We might tell ourselves untruths that we're OK when we aren't, or we may aim to numb the feeling we hold about ourselves using food, alcohol, sex or drugs. Perhaps we'll choose to spend time with others who are also numbing their feelings and also eating too much, drinking too much, having too much sex or taking drugs. In which case, we find ourselves living in a fabricated environment. In simple terms, we're self-abusing and spending our time with others who are also self-abusing; both wasting time whilst kidding ourselves that we're Ok and having fun, when in fact we're creating an unhappy and unloving environment - in which we suffer most. If we're self-abusing we're not valuing ourselves and if we're not valuing ourselves, then we're not loving ourselves.

Once we have self-awareness, we recover free will.
When we recover free will, in any moment we chose to
remember who we are.

- *Don Miguel Ruiz*

If we increase our value, we may need to change the company we keep. We might feel vulnerable or scared, because we're choosing to walk away from those who help numb our feelings, but in order to honour ourselves and 'unstick' ourselves in the name of Anahata, we must stay on track and continue on our path for self-love and high personal value.

I've always considered myself a naturally happy person, blessed with a positive disposition, yet I remember a particular period of my life when I felt so sad, I realised why the 'yellow round happy face logo' has a smile and mouth that goes upwards because at that time, I felt so desperate and sad that the corners of my mouth started to droop in the opposite direction. I lost love for myself, I felt hopeless, and went to a dark place in my mind and even questioned how I could end it all. Over days or weeks, I can't remember, I decided that I'd give life everything I'd got with the option that if it didn't improve, I might reconsider. Things did improve thank goodness. Looking back, I realised that it wasn't until I hit rock bottom that I started to climb my way back up.

Since, I've had a much deeper understanding and compassion for others in a similar situation. This is the essence of Samaritans organisation. It's a safe place to express very low feelings and emotions, without someone suggesting we lift our 'chin up' or 'put our best foot forward'.

Don't write a book!
You end up sharing all sorts of personal things.

What do we do if we've been hurt, rejected or let down? How do we heal? We might not feel in a position to move forwards, and we might not have the energy to build resilience. If we feel rejected, we may drop to our survival and security instincts, fearing and believing *we are not enough*. We risk creating stories and beliefs, that the person who has rejected us has a higher value than ourselves. Finding time, space, and acceptance of our emotions, allows our heart to heal so that we can move forwards to trust life and love again.

'There are two basic motivating forces: fear and love. When we are afraid, we pull back from life. When we are in love, we open to all that life has to offer with passion, excitement, and acceptance.'
- John Lennon

This Chakra invites us to sit and find the place in our body that feels our fear and pain. It invites us to listen to it, we can then nurture it, using our own source of love instead of filling it with someone or something else.

If I've one regret in my past, it's that I didn't spend enough time on my own. I self-abused by continually filling my time with the company of others. I didn't stop, create space, and ask myself what I needed and wanted.

Time spent nurturing ourselves is invaluable. It's never an act of selfishness, instead, an act of necessity. If we're unable to love ourselves, the love we give others will always be compromised. We must aim to love universally and open our hearts to all, yet love ourselves most dearly.

If we don't choose when to 'crash'
our bodies will choose for us.

Yoga doesn't always help us think what we want to think, or feel what we want to feel. Sometimes it makes us uncomfortable because of feelings and sensations that are buried deep within us. Poses create an element of discomfort in the body and force us to feel those sensations. Yoga poses also help us create a gap as we pass from one asana to another and in doing so, we create a space or *time frame*, allowing us to disentangle ourselves from our past. When we do this regularly (maybe every day, week, and month), we reclaim our body and in turn our lives. Yoga has been documented by many to help us move away from mental pain, bad situations, and even past trauma.

Are we making time for ourselves? Are we treating ourselves with love and compassion? Do we consider our actions and the company we keep? Does another's company, help us to numb the feelings we hold about ourselves? Do we indulge in food, sleep, drink, drugs or sex as a means of numbing how we feel about life and ourself? Are we believing another has a higher value than ourself?

We can take actions, passions, and purpose from our Bliss List. We can spend time on healthy and happy pursuits; we can roll out our mats and rewire our minds, whilst strengthening our bodies. I am not aware of any other physical sport or practice outside of yoga that helps us consciously address how we feel alongside building self-love.

What if we did love someone, want to move on, but don't want to hurt the other person in the process? We can continue to love, respect and appreciate, yet still choose to let go. We can love that person by letting them go. We're setting them free so they can find love with another. Metaphorically, placing another away from us as we would a precious baby bird is kind, loving and compassionate. You are not reducing their value, but you are protecting your own. On the other hand, suffocating others or another with love, is an imbalance in the Heart Chakra.

Physically balancing brings us feelings of calm and tranquillity.
A balanced chakra system, is a balanced soul.

As humans we want to get along, we strive to accept each other, even if we find it challenging. Bruce Tuckman in 1965 created a sequence of memorable phrases to describe the path that teams follow on their way to high performance. The four stages are named *'Forming, Storming, Norming and Performing'*. He later added a fifth stage which he named *'Adjourning'* or *'Mourning'*. Go on any organised trip or event and you may experience a similar sequence happening. It can feel like an emotional rollercoaster.

Imagine a newly formed group of people. At first everyone in the group is generally excited, aiming to get along and like each other. We get excited at the prospect of working together and even more when we find common ground. At this point we're motivated but uniformed. We're *'Forming'*. Within a period of time, which could be as little as a few hours or as long as a few months, the group will go into *'Storming'*. This can be tough, as someone will decide they don't like someone or a specific behaviour, process, or outcome. Storming is valuable for change, but isn't always pleasant and can include on a personal level, anger, suspicion, fear, and anxiety. Storming can happen after hours, days, weeks, or months.

Once the 'Storming' is rectified, corrected, or resolved, the group can settle down into *'Norming'*. That's not to say that 'Storming' won't happen a few more times but over time, the group works towards a position of success from a more settled stage, understanding roles to include boundaries. There may be a greater level of acceptance, harmony, and forgiveness for one another. We understand more about others in the group, feel more relaxed ourselves and enjoy feelings of acceptance. Our empathy may be higher at this point. During *'Performing'* the group or team are at their most effective. I think performing is similar to being happily married for a long time in that both parties know each other well, know their own roles yet work towards and achieve common aims.

As the time with that gathering, group or possibly relationship comes to an end, we enter the last stage of *'Adjourning'* or *'Mourning'* where we depart, go our separate ways and say goodbye. Sometimes we hold on though, even though our time together wasn't that successful. At the end of a course, holiday, meeting, or relationship, we often aim to stay in touch, speak or meet up again, even if it's unlikely or improbable. Sometimes we tell ourselves that our time together was better than it actually was, because it feels better to remember experiences and relationships positively, than live with unpleasantness. As humans we're designed to experience love and connection on a deep humanistic level, with that we're often reluctant to let go.

Letting go takes us into the unknown and can result in us feeling insecure and unsafe. Letting go also forces us into facing how we feel about ourselves and our own self value or worth. If we have low self-value, we may feel we need the company of the wrong person or *any* person to feel whole. We are not half of a whole, we *are* the whole. It's up to us to create and develop ourselves without the need for others to prop us up or lift us up. Understanding our actions helps us develop and learn more about ourselves.

Most people who have used my coaching services, have come to me because of a relationship difficulty or breakdown which pushes them into a state of change and often grief.

Five Stages of Change

According to Elisabeth Kulber-Ross, a Swiss-American psychiatrist, there are five stages of a grief cycle which I believe can be useful during change, be it the end of a marriage, relationship, friendship, or life. Based on her work, the below helps us understand our own actions and emotions but also helps us understand and accept the actions and emotions of another who we are aiming to support.

Denial - Refusing there is a problem. Mind is numb. Can't believe what's happened is true or has come to an end. Confusion, elation, shock, fear.
Seeking Information and communication.

Anger - Feeling frustrated around the situation; periods of aggression. Questioning. Attempting to undo the new reality. Irritation. Anxiety.
Seeking information and communication.

Bargaining - Struggling to find meaning and understanding. Reaching out to others. Telling the story (Maybe a million times).
Seeking emotional support.

Depression - Hitting 'rock bottom'. Feeling overwhelmed, helplessness, hostility, wanting to run away.
Seeking emotional support.

Acceptance - Renewed sense of identity. Renewed feeling of control. Exploring options. A way forward. No longer experiencing signs of depression.
Seeking guidance and direction.

Heart opening asanas are those that open the chest and put us in a position of vulnerability; scary but good, doing so allows us to open our body and minds to our deepest emotions, helping us understand what's really going on in our hearts. It's important to listen to our heart so it can heal.

Here are some heart opening asanas
- Bhujangasana (Cobra Pose)
- Urdhva Mukha Svanasana (Upward Facing Dog)
- Natarajasana (Dancers Pose)
- Ustrasana (Camel Pose)
- Camatkarasana Wild Thing
- Urdhva Dhanurasana (Wheel)

Gratitude and appreciation are both associated with the Heart Chakra as is journaling. Writing down how we feel, especially after our practice helps balance this Chakra.

When love hurts

I refused a necklace from a young Indian boy, with green eyes. As we travelled around a roundabout in Delhi, India, our guide pointed out a family living on a traffic island, explaining they had lived there for almost ten years, residing under a piece of plastic. She told us that the boy had bright green eyes, and many people knew of him in the area. She remembered when his mother was expecting him. Our guide, an Indian cookery teacher lived in a beautiful apartment in an affluent area nearby.

On our return in a hired tuk-tuk, we surprisingly, but briefly, met the boy. He attempted to sell us a necklace leaning into our vehicle. I looked into his young handsome face, but I didn't buy anything from him. Why not? Because after two weeks in India, I stopped buying from those who could *walk* to our vehicle and instead chose to give to those who couldn't. It haunts me and hurts my heart that I didn't buy a necklace that day, so much so that I'm tempted to go back and put it right. Would that solve his situation, or would it just soften how I feel about my behaviour?

A different day, I saw an elderly blind woman laying on her back next to a very busy road. She was extremely frail and waving her arms in the air as people drove or cycled past. Some placed a bottle or food into her empty but ever moving hands. It was the most uncomfortable thing I have ever seen and what made it worse was that I couldn't reach her from the taxi we were in. Everything in life has perspective. I thought Julia in Ghana was unfortunate not having walls for her home and only a river to wash in, yet this was in the middle of a busy, hot, dry, and dirty city. My first reaction was that this was disgraceful and shouldn't be allowed. My second reaction and thoughts were that this elderly lady was part of a community I knew nothing about. Part of her responsibility and daily purpose maybe was to collect water, even though she couldn't see and possibly couldn't stand. Someone, somewhere, was carrying her to the edge of the road and presumably collecting her. At some level the lady was being cared for. Who am I to judge? If I were to look at this differently, this lady had a purpose; to collect water for herself and possibly others. I left India loving and respecting every person and every life being lived, irrelevant of what it looked like.

Forgive and let go

Sometimes we need to forgive ourselves, sometimes we need to forgive others to move forwards positively. During my coach training I came across a Hawaiian concept named ho'oponopono; an ancient process of understanding, healing and love. Ho'oponopono can release us from feelings of conflict and bring about healing and a sense of peace. Ho'oponopono is made up from the words 'ho'o' meaning 'to make' and 'pono' meaning 'right'. The repetition in the word means 'doubly right'. Its concept states that we have connections or ties with everything and everyone we've ever met, had a relationship with or spent time with.

As we may have experienced, not every relationship is deemed successful or results in a win/win. Sometimes one or both get hurt and it can be very painful.

When it comes to the heart, using the four stages of ho'oponopono below, has helped me appreciate the people I'm connected to; it helps me find forgiveness in their behaviour and my own and brings my relationships to a place in my heart where I can continue to love and feel happy. I've used the magic of this process time and time again to help me forgive others, ask for forgiveness and to re-create or update relationships bringing them into the present.

This really could be a book in itself however, there are the four stages to ho'oponopono. Simplified they are:

1. Repentance, saying 'I'm sorry'
2. Forgiveness, saying 'please forgive me'
3. Gratitude, saying 'thank you'
4. Love, saying 'I love you'

I'm sorry – Please forgive me – Thank you – I love you

Imagine you can see the person you have a situation with, as you look at the image of them, say the words 'I'm sorry'. Dig deep and find that specific thing or aspect you're prepared to be sorry about. Ask that person to 'forgive you', for whatever it is that you've done. In return 'forgive them', for whatever they've done. Thirdly, say 'thank you' to that person for whatever you've experienced with them. There will be memories or situations that you can be grateful for. And lastly, say 'I love you'.

As an example, I went through these stages thinking about the boy in India. I apologised and asked him to forgive me for not purchasing his necklace, I forgave him for leaning into my vehicle with a little too much determination. I then thanked him for bringing the situation and feelings to my attention, I told him I loved him as a fellow human.

I reminded myself that another person is just the same as me with similar worries, anxieties, and fears. I imagined looking into his eyes. We are one. We are all connected. The longer we look into the eyes of others, the more we see ourselves.

A couple came to me for my professional services and support, they weren't getting along, and things were very fraught between them. They talked and I listened. I used the ancient Hawaiian process to help them forgive each other. That way we could create a base to work from and move towards a positive future.

I suggested they hold different ends of a simple piece of string. One holding one end, the other, holding the other. They talked about how they emotionally drained each other. Through this insight, they realised they'd been sucking each other's energy and instead of loving one other, they were resenting each other causing anger, frustration and blame.

Those who believe in ho'oponopono, believe that
if we stay in negative relationships for too long,
illness can occur over time.

I suggested that one of them cut the string and cut the 'tie' and connection between them. They were mortified at the prospect even though it was just a simple piece of string. There was a long silence, but they mutually agreed that one of them would pick up the scissors and cut it. At that moment both burst into tears. This is a good example of how much stress, anxiety and turmoil we hold within us without even being aware. That we sometimes hold tension in our bodies over days and weeks and wonder why we become so deeply sad or even ill.

It's yogic belief that deep hip opening asanas help release
negative emotions. Allowing our emotions to come to the
surface helps our bodies gently release them.

Working for Samaritans taught me there's no shame in sitting with our emotions and no shame in showing our emotions through crying or tears. This particular couple realised that by cutting the string and 'connection', they had created a fresh platform to build a new relationship, based on love and respect. It could have worked the other way, and they may have wanted to separate, which could have been right too, however this couple saw each other in a fresh new light that day. We then proceeded to create positive goals based on a win/win situation and a whole lot of love.

Every so often I go through the four stages of ho'oponopono with my family, siblings and friends. Not to pull away, but instead to refresh my relationships to where they are today. What does that do? It helps me see my relationships as they are. It prevents me from holding grudges, or holding onto situations that may have happened in the past. It helps me see people as they are in the present, which keeps me moving and thinking in a positive way. Ho'oponopono is a process in which we can forgive others. In the same way yoga believes we are connected through shared Prana or energy, that we're connected to nature through our immediate environment and the collective universe. We aim to honour our hearts and live in a place of love, compassion, and empathy. Ho'oponopono helps to create peace, increases energy, and brings us a sense of forgiveness, freedom and love.

If your heart is broken? Yogic belief is that our energy regresses into the Chakra below, in this instance the Solar Plexus Chakra, allowing the heart to strengthen and regain its sense of trust, hope and happiness in preparation for when we can love again.

Someone with a balanced Heart Chakra:
- Loves, loves, loves
- Is not overly critical of themselves
- Finds time for self-love
- Listens to their heart
- Allows themselves to cry
- Demonstrates empathy to others and self
- Forgives
- Appreciates and is grateful
- Demonstrates compassion
- Is generous in all aspects
- Feels connected to the world
- Writes a journal

Affirmations for the Heart Chakra include:
- 'I am loved'
- 'I am worthy of love'
- 'There is an infinite supply of love'
- 'I am loving towards myself and others'
- 'I chose love over any other emotion'

'If the only prayer you ever say in your entire life
is thank you, it will be enough.'

- Meister Eckhart

Our hearts feel, they're precious, they pine, they break, they tell us the truth whilst our heads try to reason. Our hearts need to be nurtured. We benefit from loving – whatever the circumstance.

Last night I had a dream
I built a castle with my hands
and put you in it
But you grew wings
and flew away
and my castle crumbled
But the next day
you returned
and sat amongst the ruins
and told me a secret
of why birds must fly
and so
I built you
a castle in the sky

- Atticus

5th Throat Chakra - Vishuddha

Expression
Communication
Listening
Truth

Meaning: Purification
Situated: Throat
Words Associated: 'I talk'
Balanced: Self-assured, clear communication, good listener, creative expression, truth,
Blocked: Lack of vocabulary, feeling misunderstood, aggressive behaviour, arguing, misunderstanding, secretes, not wanting to listen, use of negative words and actions. Sore throat, fluctuations in hormone levels, pain, or stiffness in the neck.
Overactive: Loud, sassy, opinionated, gossipy, abusing communication privileges, swearing.
Colour: Blue
Sense: Hearing
Organs: Lungs, Large Intestine, Heart Constrictor (protection of circulation of the arteries and veins)
Crystals: Aquamarine, Lapis Lazuli, Turquoise, Blue Agate
Aromatherapy Oils: Frankincense, Geranium, Jasmine, Eucalyptus

We aim to keep this Chakra healthy by expressing our highest truth through our own integrity. When balanced we feel creative, enjoy good communication, and are a conscious listener.

The Throat Chakra is liable to close down during feelings of grief, an example would be when we have a 'lump in our throat' as well as unexpressed feelings. We compromise this Chakra if we gossip, tell lies or are dishonest, if we overeat, overdrink, or create an addiction. Bottling or bunging up our problems and refusing to let them out, demonstrates a blocked Throat Chakra. Speaking our truth both externally to others and internally to ourselves is the essence of communication at his energy centre. If we feel there are clashes or conflict between our heart and our heads, our Throat Chakra can become blocked.

Yoga is a way of moving into stillness in order to experience the truth of who you are.
- Erich Schiffmann; Author

Vishuddha plays a big role in my life having been a child who, at times, wasn't allowed to speak in fear of being spoken to with a raised voice, which often left me feeling rejected and shamed. An unbalanced Throat Chakra may leave us not speaking at all, or we may go to the other end of the spectrum and over-speak and ramble.

Through the knowledge of this Chakra, we can become more mindful of not talking for the sake of talking, whilst becoming more honest and open, remaining thoughtful of others. Not letting everything we think come out of our mouths but at the same time speak our truth with as much heart and love as we can muster.

I'm not afraid to stand up for what I believe to be right. I put my hand up at the end of a training session once, and asked to speak to the host privately after he openly persecuted me in front of a room of people. As everyone left, I stood shaking in my shoes at the prospect of what I'd just orchestrated, but at the same time I was proud of myself; the lady sitting next to me leaned over and said, 'good for you'. Speaking my truth that day created a positive outcome and the trainer called me the following morning.

I'd rather be honest than be liked.

It's good to speak our truth, it's also good to listen to our own truth. But what about when we tell ourselves stories when we tell ourselves things that aren't true? An example would be, if we believe someone loves us, when in fact, they don't. We can challenge ourselves and create clarity by asking:

- Is this true?
- How do we know this is true?
- What evidence do we have to suggest this is true?
- Turning this on its head; If this is not true, who are we without this belief?

Ouch!

These simple, yet powerful, questions can help us get out of our minds and into our reality, especially if our questions are related to the Chakra below, our Heart Chakra.

When our heads and our hearts are in conflict our ego often steps in to support us, to protect us. Our ego doesn't want us to fail, it would much rather give us a distorted but happy story. Listening to our shadow can help us understand what affect we're having on our own body and mind in the long term if we're repeatedly telling ourselves *untruths*.

In a world where most scramble over themselves to tell us what they think is best for us, we are the only person who truly knows ourselves and our own situations,
if we are willing to listen.

I've created stories in my mind. In fact, I'm the queen of storytelling. I've distorted reality many times and created, romanticised, assumed and formed expectations around family, friendships, romantic connections, and previous lovers, believing them to be true. My ego has run away with me and told me things that aren't accurate or correct. I've had painful moments of truth that have left me feeling naive and leaving me questioning my personal value. And what about our shadow? We forget to listen to it. Our shadow highlights the stress and emotional turmoil we create within ourselves and if we listen, our shadow might tell us it's tired of upholding untruths, needs to rest or wants us to find another way.

Sitting on our mats and listening without judging our inner voice gives us the opportunity to ask ourselves some very personal questions.

Body vs. Head vs. Heart

Our bodies have certain needs, food, water, shelter, sleep, and sex. We too often confuse what our body needs with what our *mind* needs. We eat, sleep and drink because our bodies need to, but then we keep going because we *think* we need more based on survival and the fear of not having *enough*.

The term 'listen to your heart' suggests our heart will tell us what it feels without the assistance of a logical explanation or thought.

Some of us are emotional thinkers, others are logical thinkers, and some of us are both. If our heart is trying to tell us something but our mind refuses to listen in the name of logic, we may experience feelings of turmoil. On the other hand, we may find listening to our hearts and emotional thinking difficult if we want a logical outcome for a relationship. Without connection and communication between the head and the heart, turmoil and being unable to express ourselves can stop us from moving forward. Our bodies have requirements, and our heads have thoughts, but it's our hearts that can tell us what's really happening. Vishuddha asks us to communicate with ourselves, to have a conversation between our head and our heart.

The truth will piss you off, but then set you free.

Asanas associated with Vishuddha are those where we bend at the neck and those, we open the area of the neck and shoulders:
- Anything that opens the shoulders and neck
- Simhasana (Lions Breath)
- Setu Bandhasana (Bridge)

- Ustrasana (Camel)
- Purvatanasana (Upward Plank Pose)
- Matsyasana (Fish Pose)
- Salamba Sarvangasana (Shoulder Stand)

A person with a balanced Vishuddha Chakra:
- Stands up for what they believe in
- Speaks their truth, saying what they feel
- Listens intently when others speak
- Is heard by others
- Understands when it's appropriate to be silent
- Listen to their own thoughts
- Is honest with themselves
- Values the emotions of their heart

Affirmations for the Throat Chakra include:
- 'I listen intently to others'
- 'I speak my truth freely and openly'
- 'Being honest will free me from my current situation'
- 'My honesty attracts what I deserve'
- 'I feel safe alongside expressing myself truthfully'

Once I understood this chakra, I became a lot more relaxed and authentic in my ability to public speak. My secret key was finding the balance between my head and my heart. Found here in Vishuddha.

6th Third Eye Chakra - Ajna
Intuition,
Wisdom
Imagination
Concentration

Meaning: To know
Situated: Slightly above and between the eyebrows
Words Associated: 'I see'
Balanced: Ability to think, imagination, intuition, concentration, focus, clairvoyance, vision beyond the physical realm.
Blocked: Judgmental, confused, fear of the truth, dissociation from the real world, poor imagination.
Headaches, migraines, eye problems, insomnia.
Overactive: Nightmares, hallucinations.
Colour: Indigo
Sense: Intuition
Organs: Governor Vessel (Meridian) Conceptual Vessel (Meridian), Urinary Bladder, Small Intestine
Crystals: Amethyst, Purple Fluorite, Sodalite
Aromatherapy Oils: Chamomile, Neroli, Lavender

Our two eyes see our physical world however our Brow Chakra, often named our Third Eye Chakra, is believed to reveal understanding and awareness around our future, our perception, and our wisdom. It's often referred to as 'our teacher within' as it sees the truth, cutting through our beliefs and values as well as the labels we give ourselves (with the intent of creating an identity). We can think of it as psychic, clairvoyant, telepathic, mystical as well as that 'gut feeling' that helps show us the way towards our true nature. By listening to our intuition, we can let go of what we think we are.

Our Brow Chakra gives us the ability to look back at the steps we've taken and create a new and clear vision. Without being able to visualise or see where we are going, we may stay in the same place, possibly resulting in feeling stagnant or frustrated.

Imagination is more important than knowledge.
- Albert Einstein

Sri Aurobindo, was an Indian philosopher, yogi and guru who described intuition as 'the flash of a match in the darkness'. My intuition told me all those years ago, that my daughters' eyes weren't as healthy as they should be. It was my intuition that week, that told me to take her elsewhere, which led us to hospital. I shudder at the thought that I might have done nothing with a potentially devastating outcome. My gut feeling or intuition also told me something was wrong when I heard a strange and unfamiliar bird-like noise outside our house one Sunday morning, only to find our Labrador, Finlay, drowning in our neighbour's swimming pool. Our minds think. but our intuition speaks when things aren't right; but only if we listen to it. If we become too rational or analytical in our thinking, we can lose our ability to listen to our intuition and inner guidance. We must believe our intuition is there as a basic human instinct to be drawn upon whenever we want. To do this we might need to allow ourselves to open, or surrender having become overly sensing in our behaviour.

I went to a holistic shop in Leeds called something like 'Dark and Moon' and asked the assistant if she could advise me on purchasing seven Chakra crystals. The young lady with bright orange nail varnish, jet black hair, wearing a long purple kaftan, was very knowledgeable and knew the names of each crystal or stone just by looking at them, bearing in mind there are a few that can represent each Chakra. I came away with a little drawstring bag of crystals that I've come to cherish and value far more highly than I would have imagined. You may consider this ridiculous behaviour, or like me, you may think of the Chakras and stones as a way of creating awareness, self-love, and a base for ongoing personal development.

Taking a crystal to our mat gives us a tangible object to relate to which heightens the awareness of our practice and where we want to focus our attention.

Crystals to include Quartz, Purple Fluorite, Sodalite and Amethyst are all associated with the Third Eye Chakra which can be placed individually on the Third Eye during Shavasana, carried on our person or sat by our bed as we sleep. I bought Ellie a yellow crystal that day to carry in her purse as she said she felt she had lost confidence in elements of her master's degree. Confidence is held in Manipura, our solar plexus and third Chakra. Just the act of seeing that crystal in her purse she said, brought her awareness and helped her build upon her own self confidence. It really does work. What we put our attention on gets stronger.

It's very relaxing laying on the lawn, lounge, or bedroom floor, balancing a crystal on your body; in this case, an indigo-coloured crystal between my brows, bringing me a feeling of self-care and attention. It's comical that I place the stone slowly and lovingly back into its bag as though it has some crazy huge value, but I feel it does.

Having an appreciation for ourselves improves self-esteem, gives us time out and brings us into a physical state where we can feel our own sensations and visualise a better and more positive future.

If our Ajna Chakra is imbalanced we may feel confused, lack discipline or concentration, feel judged or judge others, we may fear the truth or idea of reality, where we're told something that doesn't match what we see. As parents we often choose to answer a child with what we believe to be correct rather than what is truthful and what they see. I remember taking my son, Sebastian, swimming as a four-year-old 'Mummy? Is that a man or a lady?' Referring to the person in front of us in the queue.

'Oh, look at that machine over there Seb with all those crisps inside' I replied. (Aiming for a distraction tactic.)

'But Mummy, Mummy, is that a man or a lady?'

Why was he wrong in asking? Why can't I truthfully answer with 'Sweetheart, I have absolutely no idea?'

An imbalance of this Chakra may create a feeling of fogginess, headaches or eye strain, denial, poor memory, and confusion that can come about through what we see, versus what we're told. We might experience detailed and frightening nightmares waking up afraid or panicked.

We can feed our Ajna Chakra along with the other six Chakras with meditation, specific colours, asanas, foods, sounds and crystals. If we don't feel we're ready for meditation then more physical work may be required to prepare us for stillness in our bodies, as well as our minds, which takes us right back to Sri Pattabhi Jois and his well-known quote 'Do your practice and all is coming'. I hear him.

Asanas associated with Ajna Chakra are those that draw our attention inwards.

To sit in meditation allows our minds to empty. Meditating in nature becomes something that I have come to value more as I've travelled deeper into this practice. My 'field of dreams' for instance, which is almost on our doorstep, has become a special place for me. I don't even have to go there physically any longer; I can visualise myself sitting in that spot. It's an ordinary, but blissful, rural British field. I have no idea why I chose it; I just had the urge to sit in a particular place one day. It's flat, shows a horizon and has a tree in the distance on the right-hand side. It's simple, open, and peaceful but because it's an open space, I can 'see' the bigger picture of my life.

The whole essence of yoga is to bring us back to the person we're supposed to be, the person we were before all the interruptions of life got in the way. As children in our innocence, we saw things clearly and viewed the heart of situations instead of how they 'should be'. Ask a child if you want the unedited truth about something. If we want to remain open with liberation and understanding we must continue to use our vision, imagination and honestly and not shut ourselves down.

Guided meditations are perfect for balancing the Third Eye Chakra, however, not everyone considers themselves proficient in visualisation, but as with many things in life, practice helps. Guided meditations help us see, feel, and experience ourselves at a deeper level. They help our minds create space for new thoughts and visions. Visualising what we want to see in our future is the first step to achieving it, nothing has ever been built without a visualisation first.

First in the mind, then in reality

How many entrepreneurs have scribbled their dreams and plans down on a random piece of paper left on the kitchen table? Using your Bliss List allows you to creatively dream, to visualise people, places, and objects that we may have forgotten about, to give things a try in our minds before bringing them into existence and reality.

Using art, a mandala for instance, as a means of focusing our attention is a good way of opening the Third Eye Chakra. A few years ago, I took a flight to Scotland, alone, and shared a house with two strangers for a week. Each day I woke, had breakfast, and visited the bakery, which was one of around five shops in the village, chose a cake and headed off to the art studio. It was one of the most amazing experiences I've had. Nothing else to do for a whole week other than paint, draw, crayon, and scribble. I walked along the coastline and as I write this, I remember the other two women being very much like-minded. All three of us took different directions as we left the house, we were very much in alignment with our third chakra, Manipura, to include our personal boundaries. It allowed us to seek and experience what we wanted - alone. I took in the fresh icy air, saw things I might not usually notice and returned to the studio filled with inspiration.

Any passive activity is a form of meditation, including listening, reading, and painting. Listening is often considered stage one of mediation and gives space to what is.

Through the practice of yoga, we are not changing what happened, we are changing the way it lives within us.

The ancient yogis, the Upanishads, sat in the ashrams of the illuminated teachers and listened. When we listen, our heart rate becomes peaceful, when we learn to focus, we cultivate sophistication and wisdom.

'I can tell you didn't go to university,' a boyfriend once said to me on a scuba diving course 'you need to wait until the end to ask questions'. I was young and impatient and found it hard to listen and focus. Interrupting others comes from an excess of energy in the Throat Chakra. Here in the Third Eye Chakra, I've learned to sit, listen, be quiet and relax more. I imagine what I may be taught in the future, which has become much easier with a bit of help from understanding this Chakra in all sorts of scenarios.

Physical poses associated with Ajna Chakra help us look inwards towards our Third Eye. Some asanas associated with this Chakra entice us to go upside-down, 'Wild Thing' for instance is a pose which calls for flipping over, giving us reason to smile or laugh out loud, depending on how physically hard we find it that day, but also giving us a different perspective, which in turn, helps us gain a different outlook. 'Wild Thing' has got to be the most fun of all inversions, I've never taken a class where fellow yogis haven't enjoyed this crazy pose.

If we attach flipping upside down with changing our perspective on life to include the wheel, fallen star, head stands and any other inversions, we can connect them with our approach in seeing life differently off our mats.

Postures and practices attached to the Third Eye Chakra relate to those needing considerable amounts of focus:

- Sitting in stillness and connecting with our intuition
- Urstrasana (Camel Pose)
- Baddha Virabhadrasana) (Humble Warrior)
- Prasarita Padottanasana (Wide Leg forward fold)
- Uttana Shishosana (Puppy Pose)
- Ardha Pincha Mayurasana (Dolphin Pose)
- Salabhasana (Locust Pose)

Someone with a balanced Third Eye Chakra:
- Meditates
- Has the ability to visualise
- Has a deeper understanding
- Paints, draws, scribbles
- Uses their intuition
- Follows their vision
- Notices their dreams
- Has an ability to concentrate
- Has the ability to focus
- Is aware of themself and their surroundings
- Resist interrupting or asking questions until the end!

Here are a few positive affirmations around the Third Eye Chakra:
- 'I notice what my intuition advises me'
- 'I see all things clearly'
- 'I'm open to my own inner wisdom'
- 'My mind feels calm and open'
- 'When I listen, I'm in meditation'

Vishuddha, when balanced, increases our intuition, and becomes our teacher from within, helping guide our way whilst inviting truth, clarity, and acceptance. When Ajna is balanced, our metaphorical onion is wide open, we learn, understand, and accept who we are on a deeper level, we become more attuned to our inner compass, our uniqueness and our personal qualities, all attributing to our true nature.

7th Crown Chakra – Sahasrara

Spiritual connection
Higher purpose
God
Love
Consciousness
Beliefs
Understanding
Bliss

Meaning: The thousand petaled lotus
Situated: The crown, top of the head
Words Associated: 'I understand'
Balanced: Universal love, open minded, wise, connected, strong faith, focused, no longer ruled by the ego
Blocked: Depression, feeling lost, not able to find connection. brain fog, tension, headaches, stuck in own thoughts and knowledge, inability to learn, thinking we are better than others, arrogance, desire to oversleep.
Overactive: Dogmatic, judgemental, ungrounded.
Colour: Violet
Sense: Beyond our known senses
Organs: Governor Vessel, Conceptual Vessel, Bladder, Small Intestine
Crystals: Diamond, Clear Quartz, Labradorite
Aromatherapy Oils: Citronella, Hyacinth, Violet Leaf, Sandalwood, Lemon, Juniper, Basil

The Crown Chakra is often referred to as the thousand-petaled lotus and could be imagined as a sunflower head bowing down over the Chakras below. The Crown Chakra is associated with expressing itself as an intelligent energy force, it offers us awareness of ourselves, helps us witness our beliefs and meaning within life. This Chakra is believed to be an operating system which distributes attention to where it's needed, and can help us feel grounded in the physical world, as well as connected to the divine. Divine can mean godlike, holy, or spiritual. Sahasrara is associated with wisdom and a sense of understanding the universe. By seeing ourselves as part of the universe, we can let go of stress in the material world and concentrate on things that matter.

There is no physical activity for this Chakra, just sitting in meditation along with living with, and enjoying, silence. When we feel balanced with the Crown Chakra, we feel trusting, blissful, purposeful, and optimistic. We feel a strong sense of self and trust in our endeavours.

A balanced Ajna Chakra allows energy to flow through our 'Third Eye', opening our imagination and helping us visualise the future, in turn pushing energy upwards towards our Crown Chakra, which helps us understand more about ourselves as well as finding the answers to our what, why and how? We can let go of the past, let go of past trauma and let go of unresolved issues. Trusting our own wisdom, and trusting that we are part of something much bigger. A union and universally connected.

Yoga was considered a religion once; if it were attached to a religion, it is closest to Hinduism, Jainism and Buddhism. However, yoga is now considered multi-faith where anyone, from anywhere, can practice. Sahasrara invites us to open our spiritual self, connecting with whatever we believe to be bigger than ourselves, to include spiritual connections, divinity, the higher self, the spiritual self, the oneness of the universe and true consciousness, separate from the physical world.

Nike advised in their famous advertising campaign *Just Do It*, Susan Jeffers entitled her book *Feel the Fear and Do It Anyway*. The more balanced our Chakra system, the more likely we are to trust in our own level of confidence, insight and wisdom and take that leap of faith with deeper understanding and insight of ourselves. When we have a deeper understanding of who we are, we can cross *The Dip* with far less effort.

'In our modern culture many of us get caught up in our day-to-day living and often lose contact with the deeper significance

of our lives. This can leave us feeling empty and our lives can begin to feel meaningless. Therefore, finding this spiritual connection is so important. The more connected we are to our spiritual source, the more harmonious our lives can be.'
- Natalie Southgate; Author

Through meditation our Crown Chakra and silence help us have both a conscious and unconscious conversation with our beliefs. Meditation is believed to be the best way to create space through silence, allowing that conversation to happen. The act of meditation gives us a platform to train our attention and awareness, helping us achieve a clear, emotionally calm, and stable, inner state. We come from nature and one day we will return to that nature. Our wisdom is realising we are not part of nature but the *whole of nature.*

An unbalanced Crown Chakra can demonstrate itself in headaches, over intellectualisation, greed or thinking ourselves better than others.

I thought myself so important. I was on a small boat named 'The Banjora' with around twelve other people for five days. One very hot afternoon, my hat blew off and whilst watching it float away from the boat, I shouted 'My hat, my hat, look my hat!' It was slowly drifting away, and I can remember feeling quite exasperated that no one was jumping into the sea to retrieve it. What was wrong with them? What was wrong with me jumping in the sea myself? Who did I think I was?

Many of us for whatever reason think we're somewhat better, higher, or more important than others due to our colour, race, intelligence, religion, academia, looks or status. I'm not quite sure what was going on with me that day but I had little intention of getting wet.

Some thirty years later, I took part in a midnight marathon walk around London wearing an embellished bra with thousands of others, both men and women helping to raise money for breast cancer. It was cold, windy and it rained for most of the night and although there were thousands of people walking, we only experienced a few hundred who walked alongside us, in front or behind us.

A group of women and I, were overtaking a disabled man, who was being helped to walk by another, when suddenly, he lost his hat in the wind. It blew off his head and flew across the street. Instantly, it brought that memory back to me, and because of his disability, there was no way he would be able to recover it. I made the decision to leave the group and crossed the road, but the wind kept taking it, blowing it in the other direction. The gale blew it down another street and over another road. I was running the opposite way, but determined to reclaim his hat. When I finally caught up with him some time later, it was a humble moment for me. He smiled and his eyes lit up, he told me it was his late fathers and that he thought he'd lost it for good. Sahasrara helps us accept our wrong doings in life, helping us learn to release, let go, and feel free in this moment.

'The birds, the moon and the clouds have an important mission: To make mankind turn their eyes towards the skies! And so, man can leave his own little local world and focus on something bigger, the universe!'

- Mehmet Murat Ildan

Someone with a balanced Sahasrara Chakra:
- Looks towards something bigger than ourselves
- Has a healthy belief system
- Lives in union with others
- Lives in union with one's self
- Has clarity of thought
- Accepts the truth
- Embraces the truth
- Feels spiritually connected
- Has the ability to assimilate information
- Let's go of past mistakes
- Meditates
- Understands we are not part of nature but all of nature

Affirmations for the Crown Chakra
- 'The world is my guru'
- 'I trust'
- 'I am guided by higher powers'
- 'The information I need comes to me'
- 'I am open to greater knowledge'
- 'I am ready to let go'
- 'I surrender my need to control'

Self-Limiting Beliefs

Self-limiting beliefs, or negative stories, play a big part in Life Coaching, they can sabotage our happiness and prevent us from achieving what we want. Self-limiting beliefs are internal stories that keep us in a mental prison, they stop us from reaching our potential in any area of life. We may believe we aren't good enough, we're too old, too fat, too thin, too weak; not flexible enough or not fit enough, the list goes on. We might knowingly, or unknowingly, sit with these beliefs and risk staying exactly where we are in life and never progressing.

In a yoga practice this is the same. We tell ourselves we'll never do a crow pose for instance and guess what? We then don't!

A coach is trained to hear these self-limiting beliefs, highlighting, or challenging them with the client; that way they can be identified, tweaked, or removed. Most of what is in 'The Dip' is how we feel about ourselves, it's often documented that the only thing that gets in our way *is ourselves*. Without the ability to view ourselves we might not notice this and instead, continue to process negative opinions for years and years. Self-limiting beliefs can come from others, possibly learned from our parents or family members, maybe from statements our teachers said, declarations from our parents, friends, wider family, or anyone with perceived authority over us. They can sit with us and create havoc.

I remember my French teacher, from when I was around the age of twelve, disliking me very much. I remember walking into her room one day and her telling me to get out. I turned around with embarrassment and as I walked out onto the step, I heard her addressing the rest of the class with the words, 'I really don't like that girl's face'. Who would say such a thing? Being told to get out before I entered the room happened too many times, and hours of teaching time was spent sitting outside her room alone. The experience left me with negative feelings and for a long time I had trouble meeting people for the first time, in fear that they wouldn't like or accept me, to the point where I had feedback that I hadn't come across as very friendly, when in fact I consider myself incredibly friendly, I was just fearful and afraid they wouldn't like the look of me. My story left me entering situations on the 'back foot'.

My teacher, through her behaviour, taught me to feel self-conscious, resulting in discomfort and embarrassment whilst needing to build up my ego to defend myself. Over the coming years, I suffered quite badly with blushing and later, acne, which left me feeling even worse! Looking back, that teacher was expressing more about herself than she was about me.

People who deal the sh*t mostly own the sh*t

As if that wasn't enough, I had an even worse belief; that I wasn't intelligent. I've learned that many people carry this same, or similar, limiting belief. At primary school, my teacher would ask me regularly to teach my friend and 'go over what we did yesterday'. I didn't mind at all, in fact, it made me feel important and smart. It appeared to prevent the teacher from having to spend time with someone who, later, was recognised as having multiple learning difficulties, something not acknowledged in the 1970s. This was where high confidence and low self-esteem showed their differences. I enjoyed feeling confident in my ability to teach my friend but was fully aware that I wasn't in the classroom with my peers and not being in the lessons that I should have been part of. I didn't know what a limiting belief was, so didn't have the awareness to identify or change it. It stopped me from experiencing and achieving what I might have and crucified my self-esteem. Before studying personal development and before being introduced to yoga, I hadn't heard of the term's values, beliefs, self-limiting beliefs, stories, or the concept of looking within. There were aspects of life that were no-go areas for years and those were the situations where my beliefs around being 'not intelligent' were triggered or challenged.

Triggers

Feeling I wasn't clever, or smart enough, stopped me from working to my full potential, and even contemplating going into further education. It stopped me pushing myself, stopped me public speaking and prevented me from reading anything aloud. I became an outwardly highly confident person whilst hiding behind a tired ego who was paddling like crazy to keep afloat. This is where we go from the top Chakra of questioning ourselves back to the bottom and re-creating a solid foundation from which to grow. For those of you not wanting to get into the philosophy of the Chakras this is where I recommend anyone to look again and use them as a platform for personal growth.

We built on our limiting beliefs by telling ourselves stories, for me, feeling 'I'm not intelligent enough' flowed into 'I'm not worthy of this education' to 'I'm not good enough for this group of people' to 'only other people are smart enough for XYZ. If someone asked me to do something I was uncomfortable with, it triggered my belief about myself and set me off in a downward emotional spiral whilst remaining stoic with an unconscious behavioural 'be strong' driver. I'd try and get out of many situations as quickly as possible, my nerves would fire up, sometimes leaving me with blotches on my skin. I might use procrastination or declare that I needed to leave the room using any excuse I could think of. I wasn't aware why this was happening and wasn't aware that my ego was working hard whilst my shadow was exhausted. It left me wanting to run away and through my deviations, I was confirming how I felt about myself and furthermore endorsing that my self-limiting beliefs or stories, must have been true all along!

Maybe you can relate to your own set of circumstances here?

This is not to say that we need to force ourselves into situations just because we've highlighted why we have refrained in the past, instead, this information empowers us to learn more about ourselves and ultimately set ourselves free. Maybe you have limiting beliefs about yourself? You might want to write down one or more below.

_____

_____

Remember, just because we write them down doesn't mean they're true. They're opinions of yourself that have been created through negative experiences. It's here in Sahasrara that we can challenge the negative beliefs we hold about ourselves and change them with all the courage we can muster.

Positive affirmations.
Say them, sing them, and chant them.

Positive affirmations are declarations or statements to which our Crown Chakra can become especially responsive. We can say them, sing them or chant them. When we affirm ourselves, we talk to our unconscious minds and help reprogram ourselves.

'It's the repetition of affirmations that leads to belief, and once that belief becomes a deep conviction, things begin to happen.'

- Claude M. Bristol; Lawyer, lecturer

Our mind believes what we tell it. If we tell our minds negative thoughts it will believe them. If we tell it positive thoughts, it will believe them. I told myself I wasn't smart and therefore not worthy because I believed that I aligned much of what I chose to do to mirror that standard. When we believe we are worthy of success, love, good relationships, a career and health, our minds follow with the word 'Yes'. Similarly, if we feel we are not smart enough, not clever enough, not good enough or not worthy enough then our minds again will also respond with the word 'Yes'. We can balance this Chakra by stopping sabotaging our thoughts, by looking at the pros and cons of our thoughts and decisions and instead create positive and proactive beliefs.

Those things on your Bliss List, are yours to grow upon.
That pose you want to master, the one you currently can't do, could be yours. The only thing that's getting in your way is your own thinking.

Only a few months ago, I was talking to someone I went to school with. He disliked the school and had little good to say about it and his experience there. 'Thing is' he said 'it's easy for you. You were one of the clever girls, one of the 'boffins' in the top form'.

'No, I wasn't,' I replied, 'I was in form six.'

'Oh', he said, 'I thought you were really clever.'

'I am.' I replied.

We trap ourselves into believing we're not good enough. By understanding ourselves better we're able to let go of our negative inner voice and appreciate our strengths, accept our imperfections and love ourselves unconditionally.

Meditation

During meditation we're in the ideal state to steer our energy up and down our spines and in turn, help to balance our Chakra system.

The first level of meditation is simply; listening. Watch children as they listen to someone reading them an interesting book, they become quiet, still, and transfixed, their heart rate becomes peaceful. The second level of meditation according to yogic belief is through mantras.

Mantras are repeated words or sounds to aid concentration in mediation.

The mantra 'So Hum' is a mantra used widely during meditation and is an excellent activity to still the mind and balance the Chakras. The Sanskrit word 'So', when translated means 'that', 'Hum' when translated means 'I'. The two words, 'So Hum' therefore mean 'that I' or 'I am that'. The word 'that' in a mantra represents The Universe. Together they mean:

'I am the Universe'

The So Hum mantra symbolises that we are all connected to universal energy, we can also name this 'oneness' or put it into a sentence, 'I am one with the Universe'. We can use the 'So Hum' mantra to bring ourselves into mindful meditation and steer our energy up and down our spines intertwining through our Chakra system.

Sitting in Padmasana or cross legged, we can bring our attention to this simple mantra and way of breathing. When we inhale, we say in our minds 'So' and when we exhale, we say in our minds 'Hum'. According to my teacher Paul Grilley, we can use this mantra to focus on each Chakra independently, and we can also distribute energy throughout the Chakras, using the same method.

Simple breath work combined with this basic mantra allows our bodies and minds to reach a calm state. It allows us to think only of what we're doing and with that, helps us connect to ourselves, our inner beings and everything around us. We can bring our attention to any one Chakra and concentrate on it using this technique.

'So Hum' is most widely used for balancing the Chakras.

Should we want to specifically lift our energy to the next Chakra, we change the words around from 'So Hum' to 'Hum So', however, just to complicate things we also change the pronunciation to 'Hum Sa' (pronounced Hum Sar)

When we breathe using 'Hum Sa', the word 'Hum' gives us a lift on an inhale, helping bring the energy upwards.

Here's an example of using 'So Hum', as a breathing technique, the Chakras, and an affirmation to help create balance. Give it a go.

Start to think about your red base Chakra, Muladhara. Visualise and feel yourself as grounded, safe and secure. Stay here and breathe into this spinning energy centre. Repeat, 'I am safe and grounded', breathe slowly and deeply.

Next, still using the breathing technique 'So Hum', move up a Chakra to Svadhisthana, your orange Sacral Chakra. See yourself having healthy relationships with others, feel yourself having a good relationship with yourself. Repeat 'I feel free and open'.

Work your way up to the next Chakra, Manipura, which is yellow, your Solar Plexus Chakra. Feel confidence oozing through you like a wave. See yourself motivated, passionate and purposeful. Visualise yourself with healthy boundaries and an ability to say 'no', whenever you like. 'I happily give things a go, even if I fail'. Feel energy rise within you as you breath, using 'So Hum'.

Concentrating on your green Heart Chakra, or Anahata, feel yourself having compassion for others. Feel the love you have for yourself. Sit here breathing 'So Hum' and concentrate on your heart. Feel yourself start to soften as you say 'There is an infinite supply of love'.

The fifth Chakra, Vishuddha or Throat Chakra, prompts us to concentrate on our throat and ears. See yourself communicating with others in a way that you want. Hear yourself speaking your truth to others as well as to yourself. Visualise the colour blue, still using 'So Hum'. Say the words 'My honesty attracts what I deserve'.

Bringing your attention to your Third Eye, or Ajna Chakra; think of the colour indigo, still breathing using 'So Hum', look up towards your Third Eye. You may find that you'll be quite relaxed here in your practice. Connect to your intuition listen to what its telling you. 'I see things clearly'.

The Crown Chakra feels wonderful as we visualise the colour white, or violet. We continue to breathe using 'So Hum'. Here we feel ourselves surrendering. Letting go of our desire to control and instead accepting what is. 'I am ready to let go'.

The Chakras and their colours help us remember and increase our awareness of our body, emotions, actions, and thoughts. If there is one thing we can do to look after ourselves, it is to create awareness of how we feel. When we understand how we feel, we become enlightened and in a stronger position to do something about it.

If we feel we're blocked in one of our Chakras, we can endeavour to come back to that place, nurture and practice asanas aligned with that Chakra whilst possibly adding specific mantras, crystals, sounds and colour. I like to sit cross legged (or in Padmasana) and be aware of my spine. It has taken me a few years to be strong enough to sit as straight as an eighteen-month-old baby. One might think it rather easy to sit crossed legged, but I have come to realise that practising yoga asanas strengthens and opens the body, enabling us to sit more comfortably in this position. Should you feel uncomfortable, rolling up a towel and placing it behind the sit bones will most certainly help as doing so tilts the pelvis forward allowing a yogi to sit taller. Alternatively, you can sit on a yoga block, sit up against a wall or lay down. We aim to keep our spines straight during meditation.

Sitting with a tall but natural spine helps the distribution of Prana or Chi, whilst enabling us to become aware of ourselves and the physical locations of each Chakra. Use your third eye chakra and imagine them spinning and opening as a current of energy rises and balances one Chakra to the next. Concentrate on each Chakra offering energy to the one above it.

Think this is crazy? You are free to think whatever you wish.
I however, feel this is Life Coaching for the self.

Now do the reverse, imagine that same energy traveling back down our spine to Muladhara, our base Chakra. Each Chakra supporting the one above and below it. Imagine this constant flow of energy up and down the spine.

Use 'Hum Sa' and 'So Hum' to delicately balance the Chakras. Why don't we teach more of this stuff to our children?

Personal development or Life Coaching had to start somewhere. I was blown away having learned some of the yoga philosophy mirrored my coach training. I've also previously mentioned that you don't have to follow the Eight Limbs of Yoga or Chakra system. You can just enjoy your asana classes, the physicality of yoga, and leave it at that. However, for me and my interest in personal development, I feel that the *Eight Limbs* and *seven Chakras* have a lot to offer in supporting us through life.

Suppose that we have a marriage or relationship problem. We have enough information to go straight to our second Chakra, Svadhisthana, as this is the Chakra for relationships. Here we might want to express our emotions, we may want to physically practice hip opening asanas, allowing us to release trapped thoughts, stories, and emotions, enabling us to let go of them. This may lead to tears, if it does, let them come. We may want to work with Manipura, our Solar Plexus Chakra to create greater confidence, healthier boundaries and higher self-esteem. Maybe we're not saying what we want to say? Maybe we're not being entirely truthful with ourselves or our perception of our relationship? In which case we might want to work with Vishuddha, our Throat Chakra; or we may want to go to our Heart Chakra and heal our own hearts, whilst sending compassion and empathy to another. We may want to revisit our base Chakra and work on our fundamental needs to rebuild and secure our foundations.

The Chakras give us the ability to identify and support a problem in our external life, or imbalance in our internal world. They give us direction and autonomy, helping us work through our emotions, thoughts, and actions at our own pace until we reach a place of peace and freedom.

Does it take commitment? Yes, it does a little bit.

I have been self-employed since I was nineteen years old. Support has been something that I wish I had more of, whether that be support from a team, a manager, or colleagues. My yoga exam class was centred on the subject of support. I shared an asana practice with an intermediate group of yogis to include a lot of arm balances, planks and inversions concentrating on the first three Chakras. Gaining strength through physical asanas has helped me feel a greater level of support in my own life.

Immersed

Seb and I went SUP (stand-up-paddle) boarding in mid-October last year. SUP boarding is becoming increasingly popular, especially with yogis, it requires strength and balance, especially if you want to practice yoga poses whilst afloat. It was another day that I've grown to affectionately name as mine and Seb's 'Boy's Day Out'.

Sahasrara, along with the base Chakra, Muladhara, are possibly the two most fundamental of the seven Chakras yet Sahasrara, I've found the hardest to describe. Below is a simplified metaphorical example to describe the six Chakras leading to the seventh.

'I'm on my board on a nearby lake. I'm balancing and feeling safe and stable'. - Muladhara, the first Chakra.

'We're happy, enjoying ourselves and going with the flow of life. We have a lovely relationship, and life feels pleasurable'. - Svadhisthana, the second Chakra

'I'm feeling confident in my ability to balance and paddle. I'm happy to accept that I may fail at any minute, lose my balance and fall in'. - Manipura, the third Chakra.

'I'm loving my son's company as well as having a massive appreciation for everything in this moment'. - Anahata, the fourth Chakra

'I'm calling over to Seb, who can hear me regardless of the strong breeze, I can hear clearly when he replies'. - Vishuddha, the fifth Chakra.

'As I paddle along, I have the ability to see, focus and concentrate on a tree at the other side of the lake and visualise where we're heading'. - Ajna, the sixth Chakra.

And finally,

'Seb, with a big grin on his face, prods me on the shoulder with his paddle and I fall (like a ballerina) into the cold water. At this very moment, as I look up towards the sky, I recognise and understand that I'm totally immersed in both my activity and the way I'm living my life. I feel unified and at one with my surroundings, the water, the air, the reeds, even the weeds. I believe, understand, accept and trust that I'm OK as I move from this moment in my water world' and back onto my board feeling nothing but bliss.' - Sahasrara, the seventh Chakra.

This I believe could be acceptable, be it hugely simplified, explanation of the power of Sahasrara.

We can only learn by getting involved.
We can only learn by getting wet.

We've been on a journey through the Chakras and learned a little about each. Here is where spiritual connection and transformation takes place. As I bobbed up and down in the cold water, I became aware I'm not only a part of my surroundings but also the result of everything I put into my life. 'We can only learn by getting involved. We can only learn by getting wet'. I'm part of nature itself and part of the universe that supports it. 'You alright Mum?' Seb asked.

'I will be in a minute', I said as the cold water filled my wetsuit. 'As soon as I can switch on my Ujjayi breathing!'

When our Crown Chakra feels strong, we feel like we're breathing in the mountain air. We feel connected to everyone and everything around us and we are in a *blissful state.*

When we practice yoga, we become aware of getting out of our heads and into our bodies, we move away from over-intellectualising and confusion and into spiritual awareness. We're able to rise above earthly problems feeling a sense of peace.

Spirituality involves the recognition of a feeling, sense or belief that there is something greater than ourselves. That there is more to being human than sensory experience, and that the greater whole of which we are part of is divine in nature.

Being aware of the seventh Chakra has helped me to look at myself and has encouraged me to look at my own beliefs and some of the negative opinions I've had about myself, others, and the world I live in. We are, after all, born to feel happy and joyous, happiness is a natural state of being human.

People with a positive disposition often ride the storms of life, and make life appear easier than those who have negative beliefs and attitudes. Many would have thought Julia in Ghana was terribly unfortunate, without the objects we rent and own, yet I felt very different viewing her life. She had a strong belief in God and through her church, she found a higher sense of connection, community and understanding. If we're measuring wealth, then I have a lifestyle and kitchen that looks like Nigella Lawson's utility or boot room, yet if I compare Julia's lean-to with some of the poverty I've seen in India then, Julia too is wealthy. We're much better off measuring the happiness of individuals and we can only do that if we live alongside others, see others as ourselves and believe we are all connected.

The Chakras, when balanced and open, share a universal energy flow, bringing us all to a place of deeper connection, whatever religion, whatever race, gender, sexual orientation, or location we live in.

My thoughts take me back to living in a shed for five weeks in India, a small wooden building with rats scurrying along the tops of the walls, yet nowhere to be seen each day when I returned, apart from frequent brown nuggets as daily 'gifts'. I felt relaxed and the rats simply left me alone. 'If you leave nature alone, nature will leave you alone,' my guru had said 'sit side by side', he said.

Last week I picked up a large toad from the middle of a pavement. It would certainly have been squashed if it crawled onto the road. I carried it for a quarter of a mile to a pond where I sat it down by the water's edge. Watching it jump into the pond made me feel quite emotional, as it seemed to sense it was where it preferred to be. We don't need as much as we think we need in life, but the right environment is useful. A toad in the middle of a road, will never be as happy as a toad in the shrubbery, or by a pond. Aim to be where you thrive and surround yourself with things from your Bliss List as much as possible. I don't yet live in a wooden building or *shed* next to a large tree - overlooking water, but I can surround myself with as much from my list as possible.

The Tree of Life

'The Tree of Life' is often seen on necklaces, it represents our personal development, our uniqueness and personal beauty. In the same way, the branches grow up and out, so do us. We too grow stronger and as we increase our knowledge and experiences leading us to a place of quiet wisdom.

Trees survive on what we exhale, we in return survive on what they exhale. 'My tree', the one I aimed to change into my swimsuit behind, is a little bigger these days. Where did that time go? Throughout my life, I've acknowledged that tree as I've walked, pushed a pram, or ran back to my car in fear of a parking ticket. We are life-giving partners on this planet with an interdependent relationship. It's ever likely we see yogis hugging trees as we start to find meaning, purpose and connection whilst embracing spirituality and a bigger interest in our natural environment.

'I only went out for a walk, and finally concluded to stay out till sundown, for going out, I found, was really going in.'
- John Muir

You may notice here, as we've worked higher up the spine that we've lifted our energy and dropped many of the emotions, feeling and beliefs we've held; we're feeling more positive, enthused and motivated. As the Chakras below Sahasrara spin, open and unblock, we have a deeper understanding of who we are and what we stand for. We allow our emotions to disperse, awaken our senses and embrace new possibilities. We start to feel confident in our ability and become mindful of self-love and appreciation. We're understanding our own truth and here at our Crown Chakra we're looking up and accepting it.

Through the learnings of yoga, I've arrived at a place where I feel much more accepting of what is. When we accept what cannot be changed, we can relax. Accepting not everything turns out the way we want or wanted, accepting not everything in life looks, appears or is the way we would do things. Accepting we're not always held in the esteem of others in a way that we wish, but that our own esteem is most important. We arrive at a place that feels so much more relaxed.

My mother and I were on our way to one of her many hospital appointments. I was desperately diverting my attention that day away from her palliative care, instead of thinking about a marketing question from a book I had in my bag.

Ask someone what they think you're good at.

'Mum? What specifically am I good at?' I asked, surely of all people, my mother would know.

She remained quiet for a short while and then said, 'You're amazing Manda'.

'Am I?' I replied.

'Yes, you are, (She paused), we all are, because we're alive.'

Maybe this level of wisdom can only come from someone who is on end-of-life care.

Life is only a short trip - we're here to enjoy it.

Yoga Benefits

Physically - If we don't move our bodies as intended, we lose the ability to move our bodies.
Mentally - We become the person we are meant to be, we return to our true nature.
Spiritually – We learn to trust we are part of something much bigger than just ourselves.

I've lived most of my adult life alongside the mantra *feel the fear and do it anyway*. I've thrown myself in and demonstrated high confidence which I'll give myself top marks for, even though I struggled with how I felt about myself. It wasn't until I trained as a Life Coach that I began to learn more about myself and how I could grow and develop, endorsed by my yoga practice. I attended a marketing conference in London where I was promised to find *my thing* by the end of the day. I was told that it was right at the end of my nose. It sounded intriguing and since I'd put so much time and effort into my studies, I went along but to my frustration, I didn't find it. It was so obvious I was told. I could almost fall over it, they said.

Then one day, some five years later, whilst in the shower (where many of us have our good ideas), I had the inspiration to write down a few words that made me feel happy. I later called it a *Bliss List*. A simple list of words that after a few weeks, told me what to do and how to live. I couldn't believe that five years of studying personal development, resulted in a life-changing simple list that brings a lot of happiness and contentment to each day.

Practising yoga helps us feel happy in the present moment. It helps us enjoy higher confidence and a stronger sense of self-esteem. Our boundaries become healthier and resilience stronger. We spend more time listening to ourselves and less time worrying about what others think. Physically our bodies become stronger, mentally our mind becomes calmer; spiritually we learn to connect through a sense of purpose. We return to our true nature, bringing us happiness, contentment, joy, bliss, optimism and positivity; and it feels nice.

Practising yoga is like having your own best friend.

I went back to visit *my* tree a few weeks ago, it stands independently, unaccompanied by the fence that once stood beside it. The paddling pool, now filled in, has been replaced by an open grass area with a zip wire and climbing frame. A lot has happened since my first attempt to find the *back of that tree.* I've done a lot and experienced a lot, no longer a child but the mother of two adults. It's a huge, humbling, and significant thought that the tree stood before I was born and will continue to stand long after my time. It continues to thrive and communicate with neighbouring trees via an underground network much the same as the thousands of energetic flowing channels intertwined within our own bodies. An energy that over time, we trust to share.

Last weekend we went away in our forty-year-old tiny caravan named Dot. As always, I practised yoga asanas outside on my mat. Later that evening I walked down the track and past a playground. Two young boys around the age of ten shouted 'Hey, yoga girl' before hiding behind the climbing frame wall. When I continued to walk, they shouted again 'Hey yoga girl'. I smiled. Thing is, as lovely as it was to hear, I'm not a girl, I'm a fifty-five year old woman, moving into the next phase of my life. Maybe you feel you're entering a new phase also or maybe life is bringing about change in another way? Yoga gives us the tools to continually adapt and adjust.

One day, maybe sooner, maybe later, I'll stop guiding yoga classes but to be pain free, I'll continue to practice for the rest of my life. I'll keep staring at my Bliss List and I'll carry on enjoying what makes me feel happy and passionate; In turn, that may again lead to another purpose. We can change and adjust as many times as we like as we navigate our way through life. Whatever happens, I'll continue to feel the fear and do it anyway.

I was diagnosed with a debilitating spinal disease over fifteen years ago. It was painful and lonely. I lost my parents, and my children grew up which questioned my purpose. I came to a crossroads not knowing which way to turn. This is what I did.

I realised both my own, and my daughter's illness didn't define who I was.

I stopped playing victim to my condition, and took action.

I bought a mat and practiced yoga asanas.

I protected my energy, and considered my boundaries.

I took a long hard look at my life, and assessed what and who no longer supported me, and stepped away.

I started eating what I felt my body wanted. I went back to being vegetarian; my family followed me.

I made sure I did something every day that I love to do. I did more of what makes my heart sing.

I put my mind on creating something bigger than just concentrating on myself.

I began to learn more about who I really am - my true nature, to honour myself and tap into the power of the universe.

Off to the shed I go,
to lose my mind and check in with my soul

Join me

- Practice yoga Asanas
- Use your breath to come into this moment
- Mix your Yin and Yang
- Practice non-violence
- Speak your truth
- Trust in your own path
- Accept you won't get everything you want in life
- Keep yourself and your environment clean
- Listen to your shadow
- Allow yourself to feel vulnerable
- Enjoy an honest practice – back off
- Listen to your heart
- Practice self-love
- Protect your energy and your boundaries
- Be truthful with your thoughts
- Say 'No' as much as you like
- Step away from the Drama Triangle
- Learn from your experiences
- Use the power of your mind to see things differently
- Let go of whatever or whoever doesn't serve you
- Take responsibility for yourself
- Practice gratitude
- Journal often
- Meditate, be still
- Understand; you are enough
- Surrender your worries to something bigger than yourself
- Embrace change. Keep adapting and adjusting
- Stare at your Bliss List
- Realise the most important relationship is the one you have with yourself
- Sit under, beside, or in trees

'Be the change you wish to see in the world'
- Gandhi

The Magic Mirror

Those arrows,
In the corners of our mouths,
They can point,
Up, or down.
Faces, shoulders,
Drooping, untrusting,
Down, towards the ground.

Life may feel quite tough at times,
Shrouded by storms or high tides,
Complex emotions, frustrations or denial,
Our authentic selves,
Hidden,
Behind a Westernised style.

It's up to us,
To change direction,
To take on life's challenges,
By ourselves.
To raise the corners of our lips,
And ring life's happiness bells.

So, come along with me today,
And let me show you,
The Magic Mirror.
Together let's take a look,
Let's share,
Let's embrace our souls,
Whilst, inhaling this dutiful air.

The storms will come,
And the rain will fall,
And life may seem,
Like it doesn't care at all,
But remember we have our own personal mirror,
And a fresh morning sun,

Ready to rise.
And other's downward-facing mouths,
Waiting for us,
To help them realise.

That we,

Are Alive!

Today's the day, we can turn things around,
And understand ourselves using,
Rainbow colours abound,
We can become enlightened,
And happier too,
The sky above,
A brilliant blue,

And notice the trees,
Eight branches reaching high,
Leaves, flickering in the wind,
Reminding us,
To let go and say goodbye,

To those old habits
Those stubborn roots,
That kept us in one place,
In our private disputes.

The magic is always,
In the mirror,
A commodity, unobserved - and undervalued.
Look beyond what you,
Initially see,

A blissful life,

Within the learnings of a tree.

- Manda

Let this book …ignite your *Bliss*

Thank you for sitting with me.
From the bottom of my heart, Namaste.

Manda
'Free as a bird'

… see you on the mat!

*'Keep a green tree in your heart
and perhaps a singing bird will come'*

Chinese Proverb

Acknowledgements

I hope my journey so far will help you understand the intention of yoga, its philosophy and what it has to offer us. Writing this book has been an absolute pleasure; checking, formatting, and uploading has been as pleasurable as pulling my teeth out with a pair of pliers!

Firstly, I'd like to thank my family, Dean, Eleanor, and Sebastian for being the wonderful, supportive, funny, and interesting people they are. Thank you for listening and helping me find the right words at crucial moments and apologies for randomly calling out from behind my computer. Thank you to Deano for tirelessly believing in everything I do and stand for, you are my best friend and lobster. I'd like to thank my editor, Naomi, for her patience in changing all my lower-case letters, semicolons, and reversed sentences. To Wiz, (Mark Barry) who has set a fine example in self-publishing and who has helped me format this book. Simon Emery who created my book cover and Geoff who rescued me after my plea on Facebook that I needed to find someone who could un-pick some crazy bat-shit stuff going on in my manuscript that I don't even have the correct words for. Geoff now lives in the U.S. and was incidentally my first snog which took place in the playground at primary school aged eleven. I remember it clearly. Someone stood beside us and timed us. Hilarious!

Thank you to my friends in The Snug writing group. I sneaked our most disliked word, 'moist' ha-ha-ha. Thank you to yoga teachers Jenny and Ryan from Leicester and Richard Voytak who was my very first yoga teacher, along with Vicky my teacher in India, all of whom set the bar high in their example of teaching and demonstrating an honest practice. Thank you and much love to all the yogis affectionately named Yoga Sheddies who have attended classes and brought both energy and peace to a shared space. It's so very enjoyable.

My parents aren't around any longer to receive a copy of this book which makes me feel sad. My father was an extremely intelligent man. He painted amazing oil and watercolour paintings alongside having many other creative talents and interests. He had an interest in local history and created a film of the history of Melton Mowbray in 1999 entitled *1000 years in and around Melton Mowbray* now available on YouTube. I miss his incredible knowledge and sadly, like many, I feel that much of what he knew has left this world forever having not been documented. Thank you Dad, for showing me the way. Hopefully one day my children will consider me hopelessly cool and a little edgy, and want to read this book from cover to cover before creating something themselves for others to enjoy.

Thank you to Lynda, Sharon, Julia, Sandra, and Holly, to the anonymous lady at Loros; the boy in India with the green eyes and the disabled man who lost his hat, all for giving me the opportunity to learn and develop. Thank you to Ralph, for giving me the opportunity to experience deep emotions and unforgettable moments. Thank you to my friends who support me and my endless flow of ideas. I love you all very much and lastly, thank you to my little dog Derek for always being by my side.

We start our yoga journey thinking we will quickly learn everything there is to learn, as time unfolds, we realise we will never know all that is on offer. We must sit content with what we understand at this time. Trusting that right now, we are enough, and what we offer is enough.

To life and forever learning.

Common Yoga Questions

What is the difference between the Yamas and
Niyamas and the Chakras?

The Yamas and Niyamas give us suggestions on how
to live our lives. You could say the Yamas tell us what
not to do and the Niyamas tell us what *to* do. Chakras
knowledge gives us the opportunity to support
ourselves physically, mentally and spiritually, bringing
us to a point of balanced energy.

What do I tell my partner when they say they're not
flexible enough to practice yoga?

You advise them that it would be a very beneficial thing
to do. Many physiotherapists use the term 'motion for
lotion'. Practising yoga asanas will keep the body
moving in all directions. It will increase flexibility and
increase the production of hyaluronic acid, which in turn
helps keep the body lubricated. A well-lubricated body
will work similarly to the oil in their car.
Motion for lotion - tell them!

Do I have to be spiritual to practice yoga?

Absolutely not! Anyone can practice yoga whatever
their beliefs. Spirituality is being concerned with the
soul or spirit.

Will any form of exercise give me the same results as yoga asanas?

To a degree yes. However, to cover all aspects of 'exercise' we might want to include muscular strength, muscular endurance, flexibility, stability/balance and explosive power or plyometric in our fitness regime. In my opinion, mixing both Yin and Yang styles of Yoga provides most if not all elements of fitness with the considerable addition of spirituality and mindfulness.

What's the difference between Life Coaching and Counselling?

A life coach is future orientated. A Life Coach will help you get from where you are to where you want to be. A life coach can help you get past what may be currently blocking you, as well as help you understand your present situation.
Should you have a situation where you want to talk, feel supported and discuss something from the past or present without wanting to move forwards yet, a counsellor is a good choice.

What does yoga mean again?

'Yoga' has many translations although the most popular is 'Yoke' or 'Unite' our mind, body, and soul. Yoga can also mean separation or disentanglement bringing us back to our true nature.

What happens to our energy?
Energy is only borrowed. One day we must give it back. We must use it wisely.

---

*Those with a chronic illness, financially support themselves
as well as use their days off and 'holiday days'
for hospital appointments and procedures.*

It's boring, stressful and never goes away.

*We often tell others that we see them as
'strong, resilient and brave'
– yet they privately have no choice.*

*All profits from this book, I lovingly pass to my daughter Eleanor,
to put towards the considerable and ongoing
costs for travel - to and from her hospital appointments.*

With many thanks for your contribution x